Australia's Venomous Wildlife

Australia's Venomous Wildlife

BY JOHN STACKHOUSE
PHOTOGRAPHS BY JOHN CARNEMOLLA

SUMMIT BOOKS
Published by Paul Hamlyn Pty Limited
Sydney·Auckland·London·New York

REFERENCES AND ACKNOWLEDGEMENTS

Barnes, J. H. *Chironex fleckeri and Chiropsalmus quadrigatus: Morphological Distinctions.* North Queensland Naturalist; Vol. 32, No. 137, 1965.
Barnes, J. H. *Studies on Three Venomous Cubomedusae.* Symp. Zool. Soc. of London, No. 16. London: Academic Press, 1966.
Barnes, J. H. *Extraction of Cnidarian Venom from Living Tentacle:* Proceedings of First International Symposium on Animal Toxins, Atlantic City, N.J. 1966. New York: Pergamon Press, 1967.
Buecherl, W., Buckley, E. E. and Deulofev, A. (editors). *Venomous Animals and their Venoms.* New York: Academy Press, 1968.
Cogger, H. G. *Australian Reptiles in Colour.* Sydney: A. H. Reed, 1967.
Cleland, J. B. and Southcott, R. V. *Injuries to Man from Marine Invertebrates in the Australian Region.* Canberra: Commonwealth Government Printer, 1965.
Commonwealth Serum Laboratories. Individual leaflets on antivenenes, published at varying dates by the C.S.L., Melbourne.
Dakin, W. J., with Isobel Bennett and Elizabeth Pope. *Australian Sea Shores.* Sydney: Angus and Robertson, 1969.
Fleay, D. *Beware, This Small Snake is Dangerous.* Vic. Naturalist, Vol. 77, 1961.
Garnet, J. Ros. (editor) *Venomous Australian Animals Dangerous to Man.* Melbourne: Commonwealth Serum Laboratories, 1968.
Halstead, B. W. *Poisonous and Venomous Marine Animals of the World: Vol. 1 Invertebrates.* Washington: U.S. Government Printing Office, 1966.
International convention on lifesaving techniques. *Hazards of Dangerous Marine Creatures.* Proceedings, B. Group, Scientific Section. Sydney: Convention committee, 1960.
McKeown, K. C. *Australian Spiders.* Sydney: Angus and Robertson, 1963.
Tidswell, F. *Researches on Australian Venom.* Sydney: Department of Public Health, 1906.
Whitley, G. P. *Poisonous and Harmful Fishes.* Melbourne: C. S. and I. R., 1943.
Worrell, E. *Dangerous Snakes of Australia and New Guinea,* Fifth edition. Sydney: Angus and Robertson, 1966.
Worrell, E. *Reptiles of Australia.* Sydney: Angus and Robertson, 1963.
Worrell, E. *Song of the Snake.* Sydney: Angus and Robertson, 1958.

In addition to the above published works, reference has been made to unpublished papers and communications by Dr J. H. Barnes and Mr T. Briggs, of Cairns; Mr David Fleay, of Burleigh Heads, Queensland and a number of other naturalists and workers with venomous animals who are generally acknowledged in the text.
A report of this nature necessarily depends on the time and cooperation of many people. One who gave early encouragement and assistance was Dr J. H. Trinca, of the Commonwealth Serum Laboratories in Melbourne. Many others were involved as well and thanks are due to my wife, who put up with the demands of time and travel that a project like this involves.
Finally, a personal acknowledgement to Dr Barnes, a modest but most impressive man whose qualities and work should one day be recognized by his country.

Summit Books
Published by Paul Hamlyn Pty Limited
176 South Creek Road, Dee Why West, NSW, Australia, 2099
First published 1970
2nd impression 1974
First published in this format 1978
© Copyright Paul Hamlyn Pty Limited 1970
Produced in Australia by the Publisher
Typeset in Australia
Printed in Hong Kong

National Library of Australia Cataloguing-in-Publication Data

Stackhouse, John
  Australia's venomous wildlife.

  Index.
  Originally published, Sydney: Hamlyn, 1970.
  ISBN 0 7271 0316 4

  1. Poisonous animals — Australia. I. Title.

591.69

CONTENTS

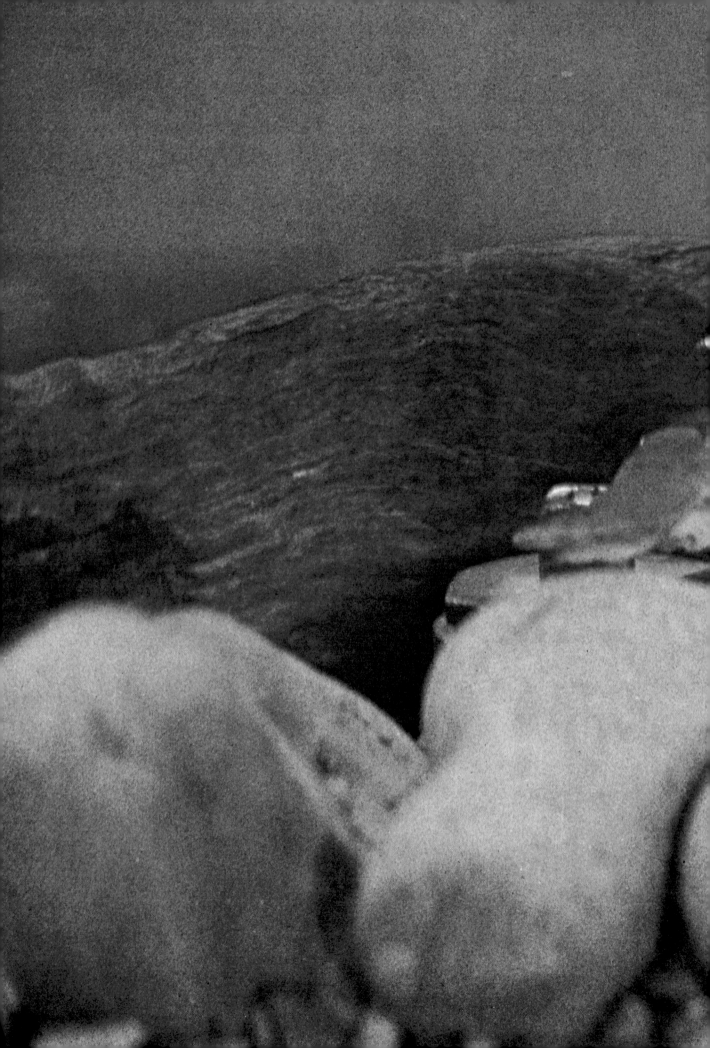

INTRODUCTION

Recently, belatedly, Australians have developed a pride in the richness of the plant and animal life of this country. We have, as every school child now learns, fauna and flora that is unique in the world. Naturalists from Sir Joseph Banks onwards have chronicled its treasures.

We now appreciate how the isolation of this continent-sized island created the environment in which our plants and animals developed. Separation of Australia from main land masses, which became absolute with the breaking of the land bridge from Asia, left this land with a natural character that many of us today are trying to preserve or recreate.

In many ways, it is as if Australia is a museum of a past era of evolution. To appreciate how this happened, you have to turn to metaphors to express your thoughts. Evolution is so immense, so all-pervading that to understand it we must compare it with more understandable and familiar things.

It is as though evolution were a tree in a garden with a number of stems growing up through the ages. In the case of Australia one of these stems was pruned and its height controlled. The tree has compensated for this by a thick and bushy growth at the curtailed level.

The 'height'—or age—of this pruning corresponds to that period in time when the development of mammals, in one instance, was passing through the marsupial phase. The other stems of our evolution tree have gone on to bear later mammals, placental mammals that give birth to viable young. The poor marsupials, primitive creatures as we like to think them, give birth to what is only a rudimentary embryo and have to nourish this outside their bodies, although in a pouch.

The absence of the predatory competition of later placental mammals meant that Australia became a field for the marsupials. Although the onward growth of the tree of evolution was cut off, the marsupials evolved laterally, to fill almost every conceivable ecological niche, from the tree tops to holes in the ground. They range from placid leaf eaters to carnivores.

In using this metaphor of the development of our animal life we make, I think, two understandable but wrong emphases. The first is based on the word 'primitive, which I deliberately used. Because something existed long, long ago, it is wrong to regard it as primitive. A better way to look at it is as successful and long-lived and as having had a period much greater than many more recent living things to develop its specialities and characteristics.

Hand in hand with this false concept of 'primitiveness' goes an even greater sin which, unfortunately, is rife in Australia's conservation movements. This is sentimentality. As I have (again deliberately) shown, we think of evolution in terms of cuddly and inoffensive koalas left behind in the harsh race towards the development of more advanced creatures like ourselves (and any true evolutionist will shudder at the thought of man's being truly advanced). We think of Australian wild life in terms of kangaroos, of possums and cute platypuses. Shades of Walt Disney! And very misleading.

As is so often the case, the true picture is more difficult to comprehend, but it is infinitely richer and more satisfying. We must be able to grasp the unique character of the whole environment, of which our darling animals are only a part (and of which we, with our cities, aeroplanes and agriculture are now also a part). We must appreciate how our fauna and flora have developed laterally with a rich growth found nowhere else in the world. We must attune ourselves to the subtleties of this environment. And most importantly, we must keep in our minds all the time that these animals and plants—almost all the animals and plants found in Australia— have been here for many millions of years. Evolution for them has not stood still. It has worked steadily to specialize, to develop the features necessary for this environment. And it is these features which provide the richness in the picture to the observer of Australia's ecology.

I have set out this concept for two reasons which are important to this book. The first is the wonderful character of this specialization in Australian life. It was the realization of this that led me to write this somewhat personal investigation of a neglected part of our natural scene. Talking in Cairns to that uncompromising worker in marine biology, Dr John Barnes (whom you will meet later in this book), I suddenly saw how wrong I was in regarding jellyfish as primitive and undeveloped animals. As a result of Dr Barnes' work, I now cannot even regard them as simple creatures. Just like the humans who are studying them, they are uniquely and wonderfully equipped for their ecological role.

The second reason is a rejection of sentimentality. By any subjective judgment, most of the creatures in this book are nasty, crawly things. I have no affection for stonefish or spiders. I can barely bring myself even to touch a harmless snake—and I am pleased to recognize that my instinct to run a mile when I come face to face with a brown snake in my garden is right and proper.

But because our Australian environment is unique and wonderful, these creatures by being part of it are also unique and wonderful. If we are to conserve our environment we must make sure there is room also for animals which are repulsive, even dangerous. We are all part of this environment. If something disappears from it, even if it is a nasty spider or a dangerous snake like the death adder, the pervasive system has been altered. Some of this unique quality will have evaporated.

To put this philosophy in more practical terms: it is comparatively easy to get money and assistance to campaign for koalas and kangaroos. But who is going to help the hard-pressed death adder whose environment is going under the plough and who lacks even the mobility to slither out of the way of man's domination of the landscape? If we are to conserve, we must conserve everything. Pleasantness should not be the only qualification for continued existence in Australia.

The way to understand these concepts is to know more about the creatures involved—and this is the general pattern of this book. I have no academic qualifications to write about venomous animals. I do not have the record of study and observation that men like Eric Worrell and Vincent Serventy have achieved which rightly puts them among the forefront of Australian nature writers.

But as authors like Robert Ardrey have shown, a 'personal investigation' of a natural subject can be of value. And this is the form this book will take. To write it, I have travelled over much of Australia and talked with many, many people. I largely report their views and the facts that other people have discovered because I am, by trade, a reporter. But in bringing these views together, I hope by synthesis that I have established my right to comment, to praise and to be critical. If I have a platform from which I write, I hope I have already made it clear. But just once more for the record: Australia has a unique and wonderful environment. We must do all we can to preserve it.

left: A brown snake striking.

left: The funnel-web spider.

left: The platypus, an egg-laying mammal found only in Australia.

THE
KILLERS

  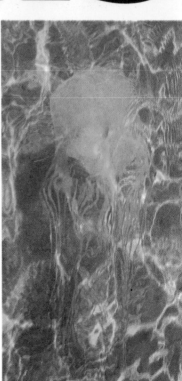

The world's most dangerous and deadly venomous animals are Australian. Man learned that the worst of them could sting him to death in great agony in less than three minutes. Others, of course, merely give an unpleasant nip. Their venom causes only a local effect like a swollen thumb.

A feature of Australia is the wide-spread distribution of these venomous land and sea animals. To put it one way, no area is really safe. The lovely blue water of the north Australian coral coast, for instance, conceals at certain seasons the deadliest of them all, the jellyfish *Chironex fleckeri,* popularly known as the 'sea wasp'. An attractive group of shells, the cones, also contains a killer. Then there is the ugly stonefish which, although it might not yet have caused a fatality, is capable of causing untold pain if you are unlucky enough to tread on it or put your hand on its spines.

On the harbour beaches and reefs in the middle of Sydney and near Melbourne, you are likely to come upon the blue-ringed octopus, whose venomous properties were little-known until comparatively recently. It has killed once in Sydney and nearly killed in Melbourne. And news reports of these incidents have brought forward other instances where the bite of this harmless-looking creature has nearly caused death.

Around the outskirts of our southern cities, you will find tiger snakes which, milligram for milligram, have the world's most potent venom. Its toxicity is about thirty times greater than that of the Indian cobra. Elsewhere and mainly in the north, there are taipans, the world's deadliest snakes. Although its venom is not quite as potent as that of the tiger snake, the taipan will, under certain circumstances, attack fiercely. And it has a much bigger venom supply.

In some of Sydney's most exclusive suburbs, you will find one of the world's most dangerous spiders, the funnel-web, and a tick with enough neuro-toxic venom to paralyse and kill animals or even children.

Despite the wide variety of venomous animals and distribution patterns which often take them into inhabited areas, laymen are often surprised that there are so few fatalities. Probably no more than five or six Australians a year die from the effects of venomous bites or stings. These figures are also a long-term average. In recent years, the numbers have been even smaller.

Not far outside the Australian natural region, however, it is a different story. In South East Asia and India, deaths are estimated to run into many thousands a year. Even in New Guinea, there is a much greater number of 'attacks'.

There are several reasons for Australia's low fatality rate. All our venomous animals on land and in the sea are shy, and the so-called 'attacks' which take place, by and large, are accidental. Furthermore, most Australians are acutely aware of snakes and do not behave foolishly. We probably also know enough to carry out emergency first aid in case of snakebite. Although about fifteen known serious incidents occur each year, these measures keep the fatalities down.

Much of the credit must go to our scientists, who lead the world in studies of venomous animals and their effects. The leader in the field is the Commonwealth Serum Laboratories in Melbourne, which has developed many counter-measures, such as antivenenes. These are now available for specific venoms in hospitals and medical centres in all areas where danger exists.

The really dangerous animals are fortunately in a minority. While many species do possess venom, often the amount of the substance is so small or its composition is such that it is harmless to man. In these cases, the worst effect of a bite is likely to be an irritation. Sand-fly or mosquito bites are in this class.

However, there is one possible source of danger, even in comparatively harmless stings like those of wasps and bees. This is a form of super-allergy called anaphylaxis. A person stung repeatedly, for instance a bee-keeper, can collapse after just one more sting in a form of anaphylactic shock. This is fairly rare, but occurs often enough to become a source of danger among those in occupations exposed to this hazard.

Even when these minor stingers are excluded, there is still a significant number of harmful venomous animals, some of which are extremely dangerous. These include six jellyfish, of which *Chironex* is notably the worst, six species of cone shells, two of octopus, the scorpion or wasp fish such as the butterfly cod, the bullrout or the South Australian cobbler, the stone fish, several sea snakes (these are not very well-known as yet), two spiders, a few ticks, about a dozen species of snakes (out of the 140 known in Australia) and one mammal—the platypus.

Of this harmful minority, only a few are really deadly. The rest can cause discomfort, even illness, although death is unlikely when a normal adult is bitten or stung. How do these creatures rank in order of deadliness?

I found it hard to persuade scientists to try to rank them. An order of deadliness is not something that can be precisely determined in a proper scientific fashion because it is necessarily a fairly subjective judgment. Interestingly, another problem is that in the study of venomous animals, there is little communication across the divisions of the various disciplines except at the Commonwealth Serum Laboratories. A marine biologist knows little about snakes; a biochemist may concentrate on one type of venom alone.

For these reasons I have compiled my own rankings. To do this, I have made non-professional and broad judgments in unrelated fields such as comparing the known facts about the amount of venom and its toxicity with the likelihood of an attack and the availability of medical aid such as antivenenes and hospitals. Applying these criteria, five animals stand out.

1. **Chironex fleckeri:** Sometimes called the sea wasp, this box jellyfish is a Medusa found for about three months of the year off the north Australian coast. Its habitat parallels the well-settled north Queensland coast and also includes areas like Weipa and Gove where settlement is increasing. It appears in the hot, sultry wet season when swimming is most attractive and hence the likelihood of incidents is great. It has been known to kill in two or three minutes. Between fifty and sixty deaths have been attributed to it in Australian waters since 1880.

2. **The taipan:** This is the world's deadliest snake and Australia's biggest (up to eleven feet). It is found mainly in northern Australia, although there is a considerable extension southwards in desert areas to approximately the latitude of Sydney. It is also common in parts of Papua-New Guinea. When molested or annoyed, it is likely to attack in a frenzy, but it is generally wary of human beings. An antivenene has been produced.

3. **The death adder:** This snake is extremely venomous, but its main danger to man is its immobility. It hides in dust, sand, or bush litter and is almost invisible. It does not move very fast and does not try to escape from man as a rule. Consequently, the death adder is likely to be trodden on, and then it will strike very quickly. It now appears to be on the wane, with man's infringement on its habitat, but when it was more common and no antivenene existed, it was a frequent cause of snakebite death. It is widely distributed in sandy areas in Australia and Papua-New Guinea.

4. **The tiger snake:** This snake is dangerous because of its extremely toxic venom and its habitat close to man's settlement, particularly the major cities and towns of the south-east. It has a reputation for attacking man, but these so-called 'attacks' are more likely to have resulted from the victim's being in the snake's way or the snake's being cornered and forced to defend itself. Generally, it seeks to escape from man and moves very quickly away. Antivenene has reduced the death rate. The snake is very common in many areas.

5. **The blue-ringed octopus:** This octopus and a related species in tropical waters are highly venomous. Both have caused death. The blue-ringed octopus wins its ranking because it is so common along the densely-populated southern coasts and is found frequently in Sydney Harbour, neighbouring inlets and also in Port Phillip Bay near Melbourne. The venom acts very swiftly but if hospital facilities are available to keep the victim breathing, he will survive with little ill effect. These octopuses are plentiful and their venom is so toxic that the question must be asked as to whether they could be the cause of hitherto unexplained coastal fatalities.

I believe there would be general agreement on the ranking of these top five deadly venomous animals. There would also be a big gap in degree of

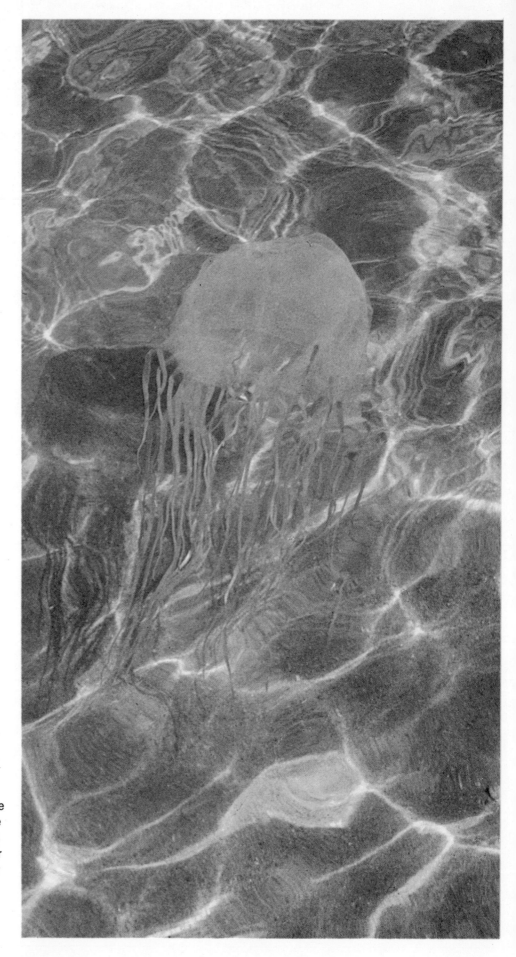

right: The sea wasp jellyfish, *Chironex fleckeri.* This unique photograph, probably the first taken of *Chironex* in its natural state, was only possible because of an unseasonal clearing of the water. When the jellyfish comes in to the beaches in the summer wet season, the water is usually too cloudy for it to be visible and swimmers are often stung because they cannot see the danger.

left: The taipan, Australia's deadliest snake.

deadliness between them and the next five, which are all snakes. In the next decade, we could easily add one more to the list, making it a top six—and this would be one of the deadly sea snakes. As yet not much is known about sea snakes, but the growth in popularity of sports like boating and diving over coral and also the increase in fishing in tropical waters make sea snake incidents almost inevitable. Recent evidence shows some species to be much more common than earlier believed and possibly even territorially aggressive against all intruders, including human divers, during the breeding season.

This possibility points to the way in which venomous animals become deadly to man. The danger results from an accidental interaction. Snakes, jellyfish and the platypus have not evolved to prey on man or other large mammals. Few even use venom as a major defence. Their contact with man and the death that results is by sheer chance.

Most animals have evolved venom as a hunting weapon for use against their normal prey. They bite or sting to immobolize potential food and sometimes to prepare it for digestion. These snake, spider and jellyfish venoms have evolved from saliva or digestive juices. They are protein compounds, or more accurately, fascinating combinations of compounds. In many cases, the working and interaction of these is not fully understood.

There are only a few animals which use venom as a defence. These include the stonefish and scorpion fish. But in both cases, appearance would be the major defensive aid. The stonefish is nearly invisible; the butterfly cod is glaringly obvious as it swims through the reef waters like a grotesque danger signal. Platypus venom would also appear to be used mainly as a defence.

After the first scientific studies of venom, which were limited mainly to measurements of toxicity, biochemists are now carrying out work on them as part of the growing interest in protein molecule studies. Protein studies, in another field, hold the key to the basic nature of life. Isolation and studies of the relationship of various protein com-

left: The death adder, a
venomous snake found over
much of Australia.

left: The most dangerous snake
of the southern Australian
States, the tiger snake.

The blue-ringed octopus, a fatal stinger found in the temperate waters of Australia's eastern and southern coasts.

pounds in venoms may throw some light on other complex protein compound relationships.

Medically, research to date has been mainly into snake venoms. It has been relatively easy to get supplies of these through 'milking'. Only recently have research workers discovered ways of getting moderate quantities of extremely deadly jellyfish toxins like those of *Chironex*.

The first emphasis has been on the effects of venom and the production of antivenenes. This takes us squarely into the territory of immunology—which is vital to modern heart transplant surgery. More recently, medical science has become interested in the potential of various venom properties. An extract from the venom of the Malayan viper is being used to dissolve blood clots forming in the veins of pregnant women. This anti-coagulant property does exist in some Australian snake venoms as well, but it is comparatively rare.

Most Australian venoms attack the nervous systems of the victims causing paralysis and death through inability to breathe. Other properties present in venoms include the ability to break down blood and tissue cells while a third can act as a blood coagulant. Some Australian venoms also contain a compound which has the ability to diffuse rapidly through the body. This, too, could be of medical significance. Octopus and spider venoms (which have a low molecular weight) are in a class of their own, but they also attack the nervous system.

The potential medical uses of venom are yet another argument in favour of conservation and preservation of these animals as part of the Australian environment.

In the big picture of Australian land and seascapes, the venomous animals undoubtedly play important roles which are not yet fully understood. Scientists and naturalists who have studied them closely have made pleas for areas where they can be preserved, where the accidental danger to man will be insignificant. Some species like the death adder already seem to be seriously threatened and may disappear if we make no efforts to protect them.

You will not get many votes in Australia campaigning for reserves for taipans or death adders. But just as much as the kangaroo or the koala, they are part of the natural ecology of the country. We must set room apart for them, so they can survive. They will probably re-establish their numbers when sufficiently large nature preservation areas are created to protect them from their worst enemies — man's machines and devastating fires.

A dispassionate examination of the evidence will show the need to allow these creatures room to survive. Firstly, without them, we would not be able to establish an authentic primitive environment. Then, although we may fear and dread them, we must realise that for just on two centuries our group of men and venomous animals have lived side by side with relatively few incidents, particularly when they treat one another with respect.

My personal opinion is that the present state of our knowledge and its requirements are a third, unanswerable argument for this form of conservation. Our scientists have been able to develop palliatives or remedies which remove much of the risk from co-existence with both land and marine venomous animals. And in the course of this work, they are unlocking some fascinating secrets.

I circulated an early draft of this material among scientists working in this field for their comments. One of them stated this case for conservation in a communication to me, from which I quote: 'Any animal, which has evolved far enough to have a highly potent venom is worthy of the most exhaustive study, not only to see why this was necessary and how it was done, but also because any potent material of animal or vegetable origin may be capable of modification to produce a useful, or even invaluable, therapeutic substance.'

If only to learn these secrets, to add to our stock of knowledge, we must conserve and live with the venomous Australians. The risks, nowadays, are small; the rewards, infinite.

opposite: The stonefish, a venomous inhabitant of reefs and sandy tropical and sub-tropical waters around the Australian coast and the Pacific Islands.

THE
SEA WASP

A warm north Queensland day in January 1955, ideal swimming weather for a five-year-old and his family at a beach near Cardwell. But in only two feet of water, six feet from shore, the boy screamed in agony.

His mother called him from the water, tried to drag sticky threads off him and was horrified to see ugly weals were scoring his thighs and legs. 'I would say it may have been only two minutes from the time he left the water until he collapsed,' she said later at the inquest.

For people who know the coastline of northern Australia, it was a repeat of a familiar and chilling story. A swimmer, still in shallow water, screams and runs out with sticky threads clinging to him. While bystanders try to help, he turns blue and collapses. About forty similar cases were on the records.

But on this occasion, man struck back. Prompted by a Cairns naturalist, the late Dr Hugo Flecker, Police Inspector E. M. Anthony ordered the sea off Cardwell Beach netted. In the nets were a number of jellyfish. These were sent back—some still alive—to Dr Flecker.

The evidence was finally beginning to come together in the solution of one of Australia's strangest mysteries, the summer deaths off our northern coastline. Although it now seems certain that both the Aboriginals and white settlers had known for years that a big square jellyfish could and did kill at certain seasons, the orthodox world of science had either overlooked it or chosen deliberately to ignore it in favour of preconceived ideas that always managed to find other reasons for the deaths.

If this situation had not existed, the

right: Small fish take up residence inside the sea wasp's tentacles which carry enough venom to kill a big man in minutes. The box-shape of the body and the long tentacles, streaming from the four pedalia can be seen in this unique photograph of an adult jellyfish taken in natural surroundings.

sea stinger mystery might have been solved much earlier. And if the solution had been discovered earlier so that a proper study of the stingers had been made, many lives—including that of the five-year-old Cardwell boy — might have been saved.

It took three scientific rebels, all of them medical doctors, to solve the mystery. The story they eventually pieced together resulted in the identification and study of what I believe is the world's most lethal venomous creature, the square box jellyfish, *Chironex fleckeri*.

On the January day that the small boy died, Dr Flecker in Cairns preserved a selection of the specimens sent to him and passed them on to the second medical man in the story, Dr R. V. Southcott, who is honorary zoologist to the South Australian Museum in Adelaide. At first Dr Southcott believed one of the interesting specimens was a jellyfish of the *Chiropsalmus* species. But a closer examination showed aspects that did not accord with the recorded description. He realized that he had discovered a new species. He named it *Chironex fleckeri*, in honour of the work of Dr Flecker. More importantly, the two doctors were able to prove it to be the killer of more than sixty Australians in the last eighty years.

The identification, confirmed in 1956, was the first step towards the studying of the habits of this highly venomous jellyfish. This work is being completed by the third medical man in the story, Dr J. H. Barnes, who still lives and works in Cairns. The studies have led to the development of first aid treatment for the

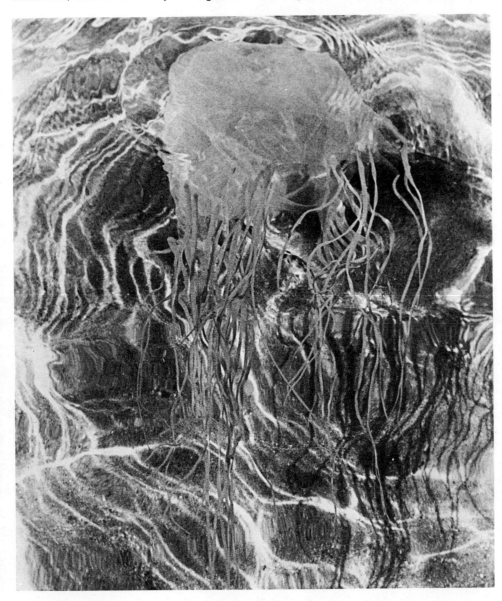

left: A better view of the tentacles, showing the way they hang from the pedalia.

The hunt for the sea wasp. Dr John Barnes conducts a late-season search for specimens to be photographed for this book.

victims and an antivenene to neutralize the jellyfish toxin. Also under way is a project which should yield a vaccine to immunize people whose work exposes them to jellyfish hazard. The vaccine would go to fishermen, boat hands and others who must enter the water during times of jellyfish infestation.

We tend to regard jellyfish as poor primitive creatures. They are indeed a simple form of life, compared, for instance, with complex organisms like ourselves. But 'primitive' is a deceptive word to use. In the millions of years that *Chironex* has been in existence, the gradual process of evolution has been refining its form, structure and behaviour. The work that Dr Barnes is doing shows that considering its simple equipment, *Chironex* is indeed a highly-evolved animal.

Chironex fleckeri is a member of the order of jellyfish called Cubomedusae. The first part of this name indicates a box-like shape. The latter, after Medusa, one of the Gorgons who had snakes for hair, is also used as a scientific description for jellyfish. Thus Cubomedusae indicates the order of box jellyfish. And as the name indicates, these are distinguished from other jellyfish by their box-shaped body or 'bell'.

The *Chironex* is one of the biggest in this order. Specimens with a bell up to ten inches long have been recorded, weighing as much as six or seven pounds. Commonly, they are described as being the size of a man's head.

The box-shaped bell is formed out of almost transparent, jelly-like material which is, however, much firmer than the jellies we eat for dessert. The translucent body often has a bluish tinge. This means that while *Chironex* can be seen and photographed in clear water, it is virtually invisible in water that has been muddied or clouded—and these are the conditions in which it is most often found.

Chironex, like other jellyfish, uses the body cavity for digesting its food (which is normally small sea creatures and often a type of shrimp). From the cavity also come food wastes and eggs and sperm for reproduction. At the lower end of the *Chironex* bell are four hand-like structures, called pedalia. From these in turn hang streams of ribbon-like tentacles, which can extend to twenty feet. It is on these tentacles that *Chironex* carries its defence. This consists of millions of stinging capsules called 'nematocysts', each of which contains a minute amount of one of the most deadly venoms man has ever discovered.

Nematocysts are far from unique either to *Chironex* or the cubomedusan order. They are the standard armament of the big family of simple creatures like the jellyfish, corals and sea anemones. The difference lies in the contents of the capsules. In most of these animals, the venom is merely enough to irritate or sting man and the larger creatures. In the years *Chironex* has been evolving, it has developed a swift-acting and terrifyingly deadly toxin.

The structure of nematocysts is incredibly complex for their microscopic size. They are thin-walled capsules, filled with the potent venom and containing a long, coiled thread, often armed with barbs. On appropriate stimulation, such as contact with a victim, the capsule shoots out its long injector thread through a weak point in its wall. This thread penetrates the victim's skin. The thread is hollow and through it flows the venom.

When the *Chironex* is in motion, its long tentacles stream out in the water. If a swimmer strikes these, they cling to him and this action can cause hundreds of thousands of minute nematocysts to trigger. In experiments, a density of something like 80,000 threads per square centimeter has been recorded.

Observers of *Chironex* always mention its beauty. Although they know its danger, naturalists who have studied the jellyfish say that in clear water, swimming steadily and streaming its tentacles, it is one of the most beautiful sights in the sea. They say no captured specimens can repeat the grace and beauty of the *Chironex* in its open, natural surroundings. This is not appreciated in captivity, because the process of capture usually results in damage, and any aquarium tank is necessarily limited in size. When specimens are killed and preserved in formalin, they tend to shrivel up.

The observations also show the *Chironex* is capable of much more than mere blind response. On each side of its four-sided body, *Chironex* has a sensory organism which is believed to be sensitive to light, pressure and vibrations. Dr Barnes, who has studied the jellyfish more closely than any other man, has noted that an individual specimen will avoid barriers and seek to escape capture—it can distinguish obstacles in the water. One result of this is that photography of free-swimming specimens is difficult. If the photographer tries to introduce a background, the jellyfish will be frightened away from it—and this is likely to be dangerous for the swimming photographer in the foreground. In its habitat, this quality would be invaluable in helping *Chironex* stay clear of coral heads and snags, frequent obstacles in the tropical northern waters.

The sensor also allows it to detect other hazards, such as wave break vibrations. Clearly, an area where big waves are breaking on to a beach is no place for a jellyfish.

Chironex is able to distinguish between potential food and inanimate objects and control the release of its nematocysts accordingly. Its characteristic food is a small shrimp with the scientific name *Acetes australis.* The jellyfish uses its nematocysts to sting small creatures like the shrimp into immobility so that it can engulf them and so that the secretions, on the inside of the tentacles as well as in the bell, can begin the digestive process.

Like all other venomous animals, *Chironex* has not developed to prey on man. Most of the deaths it has caused have been sheer accidents. But what makes the jellyfish so dangerous is not only the amount and potency of its venom, but also some of these behavioural characteristics.

The initial pain and shock of stinging will make the victim wrench himself away instinctively. This in turn will stimulate the tentacles to release many more nematocysts, increasing the severity of the dose. On the beach, the victim will invariably be found with sticky tentacles clinging to him, and helpful attempts to rip these off will again increase the amount of venom discharged.

The initial pain is terrible. Where the tentacles have released nematocysts, huge weals rise up. Often these have what are medically described as transverse bars. A layman might describe them better by saying that the victim looks as though he has been beaten with a cat-o'-nine tails made out of barbed wire. If the victim survives, the weals become disfiguring red blisters and eventually scars that may remain for years—or for the rest of the victim's life.

Medical references coldly divide the sting into two types. If a lethal dose has been received, they say, there is little that can be done. 'The response,' one handbook says, 'is too swift.' In this case collapse is followed by death within minutes, usually through heart failure resulting from massive shock. In less severe cases, there are first aid measures to use on the victim which can probably save more swimmers than in the past. But the hazard is still high.

With the terrifying potency of the *Chironex* now understood it seems incredible that a killer of this virulence remained unknown until 1956. It is as though a large part of the scientific world just did not want to know about it. The more I have read of the literature on this jellyfish, the more it seems as though Australian science was deliberately blind to the problem. In fact, the scientific establishment virtually said on a number of occasions up to 1956 that the problem did not exist.

The classic story of the sea wasp is recorded in a publication by Dr Southcott and the eminent South Australian medical scientist Sir John Cleland. This is the erudite *Injuries to man from Marine Invertebrates in the Australian region.* Dr Southcott's scholarship did not end with identifying the jellyfish. He and correspondents also tracked through eighty years of coroners' verdicts and newspaper files throughout Australia and overseas to build up a picture of just how serious a danger *Chironex* is. This research showed that in Australia alone there have been about sixty deaths which could be attributed to *Chironex* attacks, and of course there must have been many others, either unrecorded among Aboriginals or in remote areas.

The first recorded case occurred as far back as 1884, at Ross Island, near Townsville, when an eleven-year-old boy struck a jellyfish while swimming. An eyewitness, a seaman called John Kelly, saw the boy disappear after screaming and found him on the sea bottom. 'The body,' he said in evidence, 'was covered with some living matter looking like transparent string and clinging tight to the body and arm. The matter was of a pale colour. I hastily rubbed off this substance from the boy's right arm and in doing so got slightly stung myself. The matter I took off the boy's arm broke up into small bits and one piece stuck to the body about the region of the heart...about two feet in length.'

Kelly's evidence then continued: 'I have seen before what I believe to be the same substance on living matter, moving about in Ross Creek. It has a jelly-like body or head about the size of an apple, with a number of feelers streaming behind. It was those feelers I found on the child's body yesterday.'

The boy was apparently dead when carried out of the water. A doctor who examined the boy within half an hour noted the marks that the stings had left and the bluish colour of the body. He said in evidence: 'In my opinion the immediate cause of death was drowning, predisposed by the stinging of some marine animal.' And 'drowning' was the way the verdict was recorded.

In this evidence and many other reports that followed later deaths there is a good description of the 'feelers' that

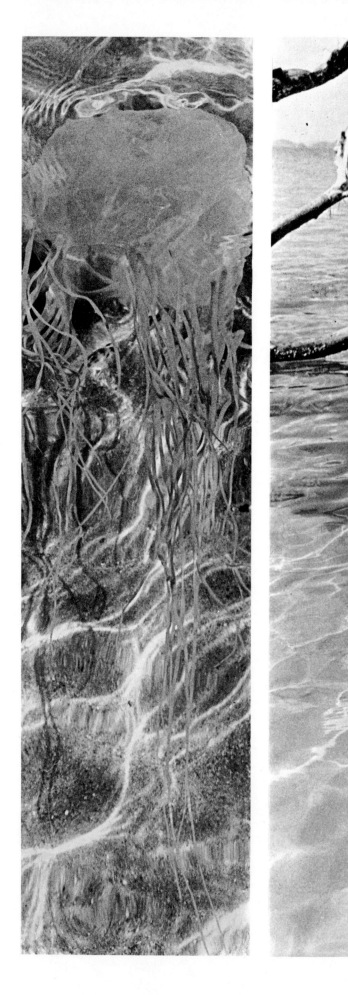

right: The sea wasp, *Chironex fleckeri*

left: Dr Barnes prepares to
capture a *Chironex* jellyfish at
a beach south of Cairns.

we now know come from *Chironex* jellyfish. Yet there was an immediate tendency to discount the sting as the cause of death and to look for other causes. Later, as Dr Southcott shows, coroners went out of their way to look for heart conditions in obviously healthy men, or even allergic reactions. There was an implied refusal to blame a highly lethal jellyfish.

The problem seems to have been a tragic lack of interest and communication. In the first place, there was an Aunt Sally close at hand in the familiar Portuguese man-o'-war, scientifically known as *Physalia,* but popularly also known as 'the bluebottle'. Bluebottles can sting and most painfully too, but they have not yet caused a death.

The early settlers and the Aboriginals had no doubt at all that a jellyfish, which they sometimes called the sea wasp, was the killer. But when they referred to the jellyfish, they usually called it a 'bluebottle' or even a 'Portuguese man-o'-war', and this is the way it was referred to in evidence and press reports. The scientists took this description to mean *Physalia,* and the line of reasoning was that as *Physalia* stings were severe but did not kill, therefore the problem was some weakness in the victims. From a vantage point in the present and with the benefit of hindsight, the communications problem seems tragically simple, but for years there seemed no way of breaking through.

The first man to identify a communications gap was a Melbourne radiologist Dr Hugo Flecker, who arrived in Cairns in 1932 with a great curiosity about and interest in nature. The tropics, he found, had all sorts of unfamiliar hazards that were little-known, of which the sea stingers were but one. He took the far-sighted and independent step of establishing a registry of poisonous and venomous plants and animals. And from this point, the evidence began to accumulate.

The next major step came during World War II. The threat to the north of Australia brought thousands of troops to north Queensland and the Northern Territory. Some of the men swam at the wrong time and were stung; several died. In the latter stages of the war, the north Queensland area was being used as an amphibious training zone and the sea stinger problem became vitally important.

With the army came a team of doctors, one of whom was Dr Southcott, from Adelaide. Dr Southcott and his colleagues began studying the problem of marine stingers and they identified several types. These they classified into two groups: type A stings which were initially not very painful, but after a slight delay led to a severe and incapacitating illness, and type B, which covered all other stings, including the very severe and frequently lethal 'sea wasp' attacks.

At this stage in the investigation, Dr Southcott played an important role. He brought to it the true spirit of scientific inquiry through his high standards of intellectual honesty. He also, when he had to leave the area, gave real encouragement to the workers like Flecker who kept puzzling at the problem.

In the years after the war, there was a controversy about the various types of stingers in medical and scientific journals. Some of these contributions discounted the serious nature of what we now know as *Chironex* stings and also raised the *Physalia* red herring—Dr Flecker himself mistakenly attributed some deaths to the 'Portuguese man-o'-war'. But he steadily continued the process of gathering evidence and classifying the results so that the nature of the type B lethal stings became much clearer.

Dr Flecker also was able to define in detail the symptoms of the army men's type A stinger. For reference purposes, he gave it the name 'Irukandji', the tribal name of Aboriginals in the Cairns area. With the Irukandji sting symptoms described and the sea wasp sting more clearly defined, the stage was set by the mid 1950s for concrete discovery.

The first breakthrough came on that January day in 1955. Dr Flecker and Dr Southcott were able to show that a previously unrecorded jellyfish was the villain responsible for the fatalities.

The third medical man in the *Chironex* story, Dr John Barnes, had not up to this time been intimately concerned in the investigation. At a medical congress, he passed on some Aboriginal knowledge he had gained to Dr Flecker. 'Dr Flecker

opposite: The sea wasp photographed on a clear, sandy bottom. The structure of its streaming tentacles, which contain the massive stinging mechanism can be clearly seen. At times, these tentacles can stretch to more than eight feet in length.

lambasted me for not telling him earlier,' Dr Barnes recalls. 'I, too, was guilty of this failure to communicate.'

This incident was to have a significant sequel. After the identification of *Chironex,* Dr Flecker was generally believed to be continuing his studies of the jellyfish and also his hunt for the then unknown Irukandji stinger. However, he died suddenly in June 1957 and his records were never discovered. Dr Barnes, moved partly by the memory of the incident at the medical congress, stepped in to carry on the work. At first he hoped to find Dr Flecker's notes and prepare them for publication, but these were never traced. Dr Barnes found he

above: Dr John Barnes, who played a major part in the research which has led to an understanding of the deadly sea wasp.

was picking up the threads from Dr Flecker to become the third medical man in this long investigation.

The role of Dr Barnes was to be a new one—the classic second stage of scientific investigation, the period of observation and experiment. Dr Barnes was in a position to combine clinical observation and records of injuries with a vast amount of field investigation. His aim was to establish a correlation between the injuries and the animal that caused them.

John Barnes is a short, greying man of western Queensland origin. The demands of his practice in Cairns clearly press on him and eat into his time. The research programme for him became forays into the field, whenever he could get away, swimming alongside and studying the *Chironex* jellyfish, capturing them, keeping them in an aquarium and continuously recording the results of these observations. Dr Barnes brought to this difficult task what one scientific commentator described to me as: 'The precision this subject badly needed.'

He worked first to recover nematocysts from the skins of victims of stingers and compare these with capsules recovered from jellyfish present in the area at the time. This was no armchair quest by any means—at times it was downright dangerous. The first result of his programme of observations was to bring together the information which now allows *Chironex* to be identified quickly in the season and warnings of its presence to be issued. As he studied its habits and the nature of its responses to stimuli, he was finally able to develop a simple first aid treatment for its stings.

In a series of scientific papers, Dr Barnes described these characteristics and observations. *Chironex,* he says, comes into tropical coasts when seasonal changes reduce the turbulence of waters around the northern coastline and the first river run-offs from summer storms lower the salinity. At first Dr Barnes believed *Chironex* spent the dry season in the open ocean. Now, it appears more likely that it submerges in deeper water closer to the coast, between the barriers of coral reefs. As I have mentioned, *Chironex* feeds mainly on the small shrimp *Acetes australis.*

When this shrimp comes in to the beaches, it is a danger signal that *Chironex* is also likely to be present.

Dr Barnes also watched the jellyfish feed on the shrimps, stinging them into immobility then carrying them into the body cavity for digestion. He obtained the first pure samples of venom by inducing *Chironex* to sting a human membrane stretched over a collecting vessel. Later he found he was able to secure greater quantities of venom by making tentacles discharge without the presence of the membrane. This has resulted in what is, comparatively, a massive venom yield. The venom is not as pure as the 'milked' venom, he says, but a remarkable degree of purity can be achieved by fractional separation.

This securing of venom has cleared the way for an antivenene to be produced. An antivenene is a substance derived in the body of an animal and designed to attack the toxin and neutralize it in a victim's body.

The venom also appears to be a fascinating chemical compound. Dr Barnes and other workers have found it highly unstable and likely to deteriorate very rapidly in all but ideal conditions. Supplies of venom are now being studied at the University of Queensland and there is also interest in the project overseas.

The study of the *Chironex's* stinging mechanism and of the venom itself has led to the new procedures for saving life. Dr Barnes now recommends that when a person is stung, the victim should be taken from the water as quickly as possible, that tourniquets be applied to the affected limbs—if this is possible—and that copious quantities of an alcohol like methylated spirits be poured over the sticky tentacles. The spirit will inactivate the nematocysts and shrivel the tentacles, so that they can be brushed off without the danger of releasing more venom.

Dr Barnes' work has shown the danger of trying to wash off tentacles or pull them off. Instinctive treatment like this in the past could have resulted in the release of more nematocysts and venom and thus some of the earlier deaths.

The theory now is that the venom kills quickly through massive chemical shock.

If the action is slowed down and the dose minimized, the body can cope and rally to eventual recovery. The methylated spirits method should give the time to allow the victim to be taken to hospital for specialized treatment, and, when it becomes available, with the new antivenene now being prepared.

Although the sea wasp danger is little-known outside northern Australia, there is little mistaking the immense impact which Dr Barnes' work has had in tropical areas. In north Queensland, posters everywhere provide descriptions of the lethal jellyfish and the danger signals which herald its coming. The methylated spirits first aid method is also well publicized and many fishermen and bathers now include a gallon of methylated spirits in their kit.

Throughout the season, radio and television carry specific warnings as to when the danger is likely to be at its height. This allows northerners to avoid hazard. They are now more confident, as well, that if they are stung new procedures are available which greatly increase their chances of survival.

Dr Barnes regards his work on *Chironex* as being far from completed. His programme of observations is revealing new facts about the jellyfish, including the possibility of social behaviour patterns which have not been observed before among the simpler animals.

He has extended his work to other marine stingers, including the Irukandji. Dr Barnes has found that a small cubomedusan species causes this serious but non-fatal sting. This jellyfish, very different from the big Cubomedusae, has now been identified as a new species and has been called *Carukia barnesi*.

The *Carukia* stinger, only about an inch long, is transparent and mixes with other small jellyfish. It is almost impossible to see or net. To date, only a few samples have been captured although, as injuries to swimmers show, at times the stinger is distressingly common in the Cairns area.

Dr Barnes proved the identity of this stinger by deliberately letting the specimen sting him on the arm. He then coolly recorded the mild skin reddening and the other characteristic symptoms. Nothing happened for the first twenty minutes. Then the severe illness, with its unpleasant symptoms, made itself felt. The illness begins with backache, chest and abdominal pains and vomiting and can last some weeks. As yet there is no antidote, although medical treatment can relieve some of the symptoms of Irukandji illness.

This long and risky investigation, which has shown the existence of the world's most dangerous venomous animal off the Australian coast, provides a typical case of one aspect of the Australian's attitude to his own country and people. The hunt for the alleged Noah's ark on Mount Ararat or the very hypothetical Loch Ness monster is far better known in Australia than the solution of a true-life mystery right on our doorstep.

I pose the question whether this trait did not, in fact, help our marine scientists virtually to ignore the existence of *Chironex* and its unpleasant companion *Carukia* for all those years when Australians were either dying or becoming seriously ill. This quest was clearly one which demanded attention —and money—much earlier than the time when it finally came under scientific scrutiny. If it had been solved earlier, the chances are that many people, most of them children, would be alive today.

The lesson that emerges, I think, is the importance of true scientific method and application. The discoveries by the three medical men, Flecker, Southcott and Barnes hark back to the days when scientists were more general in their approach than today. And in the broad-spectrum approach of medically-trained workers, the best path lay towards its solution.

I would like to think that the solution of the *Chironex*/Irukandji mystery means that no unknown dangers are left on our coasts. One scientist to whom I made this confident assertion smartly set me back on my heels. 'How, in the light of what we know now about *Chironex*, can anyone be sure?' he said. Certainly, if nature can endow a simple jellyfish with the most potent killing mechanism of any venomous animal, we must expect that there will be other surprises in store as we begin to use and explore more thoroughly our tropical sea and coasts.

OCTOPUS AND CONE SHELLS

The Blue-Ringed Octopus

If the scientific fault of refusing to believe that a primitive creature like a jellyfish could be dangerous was the problem that hid the identity of the *Chironex* sea wasp for so long, the other cardinal sin of man's relations with nature — sentimentality — was equally fatal in the case of the venomous octopus.

Even today when the deadliness of the small blue-ringed octopus is known, it is hard to believe that this funny little animal is a killer. Really, you think, it could be a fugitive from a Disney movie.

As you examine it—possibly poke it with a stick—the bands around its tentacles start to glow blue. But keep in mind that warning signals in nature do not always glow red—in this case blue spells danger. This funny little octopus is the second biggest venomous danger on the Australian coast. On two occasions — two known occasions — small octopus have killed people in Australia. At both times, the death occurred because the victim was playing with the comic-looking creature. There are several other recorded instances of 'attacks' when the victims did not die, but were dangerously sick. And on every occasion, the people were playing with the octopus.

There are two venomous octopus species off the Australian coast: the blue-ringed octopus, which is very common in our populated areas, and a closely-related one found in the tropics.

The blue-ringed octopus is known scientifically as *Hapalochlaena maculosa.* It is found along the Australian coast between southern Queensland and South Australia and is probably most common in New South Wales and Victoria. I have seen this octopus on rocks at an inlet north of Sydney—in what is now the outer suburbs—and there have been many instances of its being seen in Sydney Harbour, Botany Bay and Port Phillip, Victoria. In fact, one of the fatalities occurred at Camp Cove, near the entrance to Sydney Harbour, and a near fatality occurred on a bay beach just outside Melbourne.

The Sydney death was that of a young soldier in 1967. The publicity that this created brought home to the general public for the first time the danger of foolish contact with the octopus. It also started a research programme into the octopus and its venom which, at the time of writing, is still under way and on the verge of yielding significant scientific information.

Australia's other known octopus death occurred in Darwin in 1954. This time the victim was a young seaman and the villain was identified as a close relative of the southern blue-ringed octopus, known scientifically as *Octopus lunulata.*

If you keep your eyes open along the reefs and bays of our south-east coast, it is quite possible that you or your children will find the interesting blue-ringed octopus. It is only tiny, rarely more than six inches across and commonly between three and four inches. It has a true octopus shape, is browny-speckled in colour and has distinctive blue bands around its tentacles which give it its name. When annoyed or excited, the octopus seems to flash a warning by stimulating these bands to a brilliant electric blue. Generally, it lives on reefs and in rock pools.

Most victims have taken the little octopus out of the water and put it on their hand or arm to show it to someone. In the Darwin incident, the skylarking sailor had draped *O. lunulata* over his bare shoulder. At Camp Cove, the young soldier had placed a blue-ringed octopus on his forearm.

In these circumstances, the octopus colours brilliantly, then pierces the skin with its beak. This injects a dose of highly toxic venom, capable of rapid diffusion through the body. The toxin

below: The blue-ringed octopus. The tube feet can be clearly seen on the undersides of the tentacles.

paralyses control centres and the known victims have died through suffocation.

The remedy is to maintain respiration artificially, beginning immediately with mouth-to-mouth resuscitation, transferring the victim to an iron lung as soon as possible. This procedure saved the life of a thirty-three-year-old man at Beaumaris, Melbourne, in July 1962. The Alfred Hospital Clinical Research Unit compiled what is now regarded as a classic report on an octopus bite: 'The patient held it on the back of the hand for a minute or two and, after putting it down, noticed a speck of blood on his hand. There had been no sensation of a sting or a bite. A few minutes later he

The blue-ringed octopus, photographed in a display tank as it might be found in nature in a rocky environment.

felt a prickling sensation around his mouth which rapidly became generalized and within fifteen minutes was almost completely paralysed. (In a newspaper interview, the victim said that a few minutes after noticing the speck of blood, his hand started to tingle. Then tingling of the lips followed.)

'He was hardly able to breathe. After half an hour he began vomiting and "convulsing".

'On arrival here (the Alfred Hospital) about one hour after the onset, he was still breathing and was not cyanosed. He was fully conscious and understood

pital with the patient and was positively identified as *Octopus* (now changed to *Hapalochlaena*) *maculosa.'*

The Beaumaris incident came close to death and research work began immediately. Workers turned up several other cases in which octopus bites had led to severe, although temporary, paralysis. The publicity led to the discovery of other well-authenticated cases in which medical records had not been reported—another instance of the communications gap on venomous creatures. The Camp Cove case made it clear that the small octopus was a menace.

our conversation . . . . There was no muscle tone, no fibrillation, no reflexes and there was complete paralysis, including pharyngeal paralysis. He was, however, able to move his diaphragm and half open his eyes. There was a tiny red spot on the back of his left hand . . . . Just after an hour spontaneous respiration ceased and he was respired for about an hour.

'Thereafter, he made a steady and uneventful recovery of his muscle power. He was well the next day, chest X-ray was clear and he was discharged. The octopus in this case came to the hos-

These photographs display the swimming action of the octopus. It moves through the water by expelling a jet which thrusts it along. The characteristic blue rings can be seen on its tentacles.

To my mind, its big danger is to children. Firstly, in their play on beaches and rock pools they are likely to find and try to handle the octopus. Secondly, because they are smaller, the venom will have a more severe effect. The toxicity of venom normally varies with the body weight; for instance, it takes a smaller dose to kill a mouse than a guinea pig. Similarly, for a given dose, a lighter child will be more seriously affected than an adult. And in both known fatalities, octopus venom has killed fit and healthy young men.

Much work remains to be done on

the octopus and its venom. But the general observation up to the present time is that the octopus will bite man only when it is taken out of the water and aroused. Naturalists I have spoken to say they believe the octopus might eventually be credited with other deaths among the numbers of unexplained marine disappearances that occur every year.

In the case of the jellyfish, it was not until a long and laborious search of inquest and press reports was completed that it became clear just how many Australians *Chironex* had killed. A

be no obvious sign of the fast-acting toxin and indications would be the same as death by drowning. The bite is hard to find at the best of times, let alone on a water-affected body.

Work on the octopus is going ahead at a good pace. Researchers in Queensland, in Sydney and at the Commonwealth Serum Laboratories in Melbourne have received good supplies of octopus venom and are investigating its properties. It seems that this work is unlikely to result in an early antidote for the octopus venom. This is mainly because of problems associated with the mole-

similar study of the likelihood of an octopus sting, related to disappearances of people like experienced rock fishermen, might well show a similar correlation.

Take the hypothetical case of a lone fisherman finding an octopus, possibly even planning to use it as bait. The bite would be imperceptible and the first effect, already studied clinically, is muscular paralysis. The victim could die either from drowning or suffocation. In many instances the body would be swept away and not recovered. If the body were found, however, there would

cules of the compounds present in the venom. But already clinical work has shown the need to maintain respiration of victims and, if this is done, there seems no reason why any victim with a companion need die in the future.

But as with all venomous creatures, the important thing is to avoid a bite in the first instance. And the easiest way to do this is to keep clear of these two octopuses. Laugh at them if you will, even poke one of them (with a stick) as I have done to make it angry and to make its blue bands glow. But never, never, playfully pick it up.

Cone Shells

The same advice applies to another one of our venomous sea creatures which although very different has a number of features in common with the octopus. This is the attractive, but venomous cone shell, which is found in tropical waters around Australia and Papua-New Guinea —and notably on the Barrier Reef. At least one cone has killed in Australia and possibly three or four of them are potentially lethal. There are records of about five cone shell deaths in the Pacific region in recent years. And there must have been fatalities in the past among Queensland coastal Aboriginal groups and island people, because in native tradition the venomous properties of the cone are well understood.

The New Guinea shell enthusiast Fred Kleckham has collected more than seventy species of cone shell from the waters around one island alone, Manus in the Admiralty Group, to the north of New Guinea. Six species were recognized as dangerous. The Manus Island people have word-of-mouth traditions of several cases where people have been bitten. One fatal victim was said to have been an American serviceman who died during the war.

The active marine biologists of Queensland University, headed by the Barrier Reef authority Dr Robert Endean have carefully studied Queensland cone shells and reached the conclusion that three of them have dangerous venom. These are the *Conus* species *geographus, catus* and *tulipa*. Dr Endean and his co-worker Clare Rudkin said the first two of these were known to prey on fish, while it was likely the third one did as well.

The waters of Australia's beautiful coastline harbour many of our deadliest creatures.

Research in other areas shows that it is mainly the fish-eating cone shellfish which have venom. They use it to immobilize the tiny fish which they eat. Experiments have shown that injections of venom kill these fish in seconds. The cone shellfish, like its remote relative the octopus, is comparatively slow-moving and needs this additional weapon to secure its prey.

Despite the investigatory work that has been done into the cone shellfish, there is still some doubt as to exactly how its venom mechanism works. Scientists have traced the venom duct and know that the venom is injected by means of teeth, contained on a proboscis which is normally retracted into the shell. One theory is that the tooth is retracted into a pool of venom. When the tooth is extended during an attack, it is able to break the skin of the victim and inject the venom. Human victims of the conefish have in all instances been handling the shellfish before they were bitten.

The Australian fatality occurred on Hayman Island in 1935. The victim was a young man, fit and in good health, who was holding the shell in his hand while he scraped it. The shell was that of *Conus geographus.* (The record of the event comes through Dr Flecker whose work on *Chironex* has been discussed previously. This is another example of the value of his work on venomous dangers.)

While the man was holding the shell, the fish inside extended its proboscis and stung him on the palm. According to witnesses, 'just a small puncture mark' was visible. Other symptoms were remarkably similar to what we now know about octopus bites. The victim's mother said the man started complaining of a numb feeling. His lips became stiff, then his sight blurred and he experienced double vision. At thirty minutes his legs were paralysed and within the hour he was unconscious and drifting into a coma. Another witness present on the cruise boat agreed with the onset of symptoms, but reported a longer period before the victim drifted into his fatal coma.

In this case, in documented New Guinea cases and in another Australian 'attack' this time at Hope Island on the reef, observers noted problems with breathing. At Manus Island in 1954, a medical assistant, called to treat a seven-year-old native girl who had been stung, got his medical orderlies to apply artificial respiration to the victim while he rigged up what was described as a 'Heath Robinson' artificial lung out of (among other things) 'a rubber tube and a football bladder'. The girl was kept breathing for more than three hours and later recovered. From this experience, medical opinion has agreed that as in the case of octopus bite, victims can be saved if they are kept breathing.

Dr Endean points out that the *geographus* shell, which killed the man on Hayman Island, is also comparatively rare so the possibility of a fatal sting is remote. Nevertheless, the advice given in medical texts is to treat all cone shells with care. Experienced collectors advise that the best way is to regard them all as potentially dangerous. They usually pick up this type of shell at the 'big end', because the proboscis emerges from the pointed end—the apex of the cone. However, the shellfish inside is fairly dexterous and as it could still reach back to jab a finger with venom, the best recommendation is either to leave cone shells alone or handle them only with forceps. One mistake is to carry them either in a bag swinging against the body or in a pocket. There are several instances on record where they have stung severely through a layer of cloth.

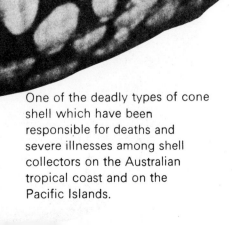

One of the deadly types of cone shell which have been responsible for deaths and severe illnesses among shell collectors on the Australian tropical coast and on the Pacific Islands.

FISH AND
SEA SNAKES

All the venomous animals described so far have had one characteristic in common—they are all without a back-bone. They belong to that vast class of what we sometimes regard as 'simple' or 'primitive' creatures called Invertebrates. But most of the venomous creatures we know better do have backbones; they are called Vertebrates.

Two groups of vertebrate animals which have dangerous and venomous members in Australia share the sea environment with jellyfish, octopus and cones. These are fish and reptiles.

There is something about the appear-ance of the dangerous fish that tells us they are likely to be poisonous if we try to use them for food, or venomous, in that they might harm us if we handle them. If we go fishing, for instance, a snapper or mackerel on the line is a completely different proposition from a toad fish. We know the former is good to eat; the latter is doubtful.

By and large, the venomous fish look downright mean and nasty. Some of them are easily seen—the butterfly cod, for instance is a swimming danger signal. Others, like the stonefish, are almost impossible to see in their natural surroundings.

The Stonefish

Stonefish are so well camouflaged and look so much like chunks of old coral half buried in the sand that even experts find it hard to see them under open reef conditions. And it is this quality of invisibility that makes them so danger-ous. A person walking or swimming on the reef is likely to tread on one or put his hand on it, and it is then that its venom mechanism comes into play.

Stonefish have thirteen spines along their backs, and each spine is supplied with venom from two glands. The pres-sure of a person's weight can drive the spines deep into the skin, injecting venom into the flesh of the feet or hands. The result is an intense, blinding pain that is all but unbearable. The main danger comes from the probability of collapse. The unconscious victim is likely to drown. Muscles close to the wounds will become swollen and this symptom will spread with the venom. As the swelling increases, so will the pain.

The Commonwealth Serum Labora-tories, which has developed an antidote to the venom, recommends keeping the victim breathing by artificial respiration.

right: The immobile stonefish looks so like a piece of rock or coral that it attracts weeds and other sea infestations, which complete its camouflage. From only a few inches away it is, to the untrained eye, completely invisible. This picture was taken at Green Island's Marineland.

Medical aid—and an antivenene—should be secured as quickly as possible. Until this comes, you can also assist a victim by trying to relieve the excruciating pain by immersing the leg or hand in hot water and applying hot fomentations. The pain and toxic effect of the venom can result in death. There is one instance of death from heart failure. But given assistance, victims are unlikely to die from the direct effects of the venom.

The stonefish and other related venomous fish appear to use their venom mechanism purely for defence. The stonefish usually remains immobile; it lurks in surroundings suiting its camouflage until either it is disturbed by man or one of the small fish on which it preys swims past. When it wants to feed, its action is incredibly swift.

The curator of Green Island Marineland, Al Miller, demonstrated this for me. He dropped some food in the stonefish tank. The fish snapped it up so quickly I did not even see the motion, even though I was looking for it.

The stonefish can be found from Moreton Bay northwards in Queensland, right around Papua and New Guinea and the Pacific Islands and, of course, in equivalent Western Australian and Northern Territory waters. There are three species of the fish, with only minor differences between them. All can sting badly. Although you seldom see it, the stonefish is common.

The danger lies in the fact that it will make no move to avoid you. It will just lie there until you tread on it or put your hand on it. And it is not much good depending on being able to see the fish as you move along. Stonefish camouflage is virtually perfect.

If you cannot see the stonefish and it will not avoid you, the only avenue is to protect yourself as much as possible. This is one of the main reasons why local people always insist you wear shoes when you are exploring coral reefs and sandy areas. Flimsy shoes are not good protection. Cases of stonefish spines penetrating rubber-soled or canvas shoes are fairly common.

The ugly stonefish is worth all the respect you can give him. His dual system of protection, camouflage backed up by a fearsome weapon, is a strong combination in his environment.

The Butterfly Cod

That flamboyant cousin of the stonefish, the butterfly cod or the scorpion fish as it is sometimes known, protects itself in an entirely different way.

My first sight in nature of one of these was while diving off a reef near Port Moresby, in Papua. I came almost face to face with a magnificent red and purpled-coloured specimen drifting through the coral like a warlord in a Chinese opera, pugnacious and frightening, trailing vast silken banners. Its colour and horrible appearance were unmistakable warnings that this fish was dangerous. I sheered off at a safe distance and eventually retreated from the area in case I should accidentally swim into it while I was on the surface.

The warning appearance serves it well. Like the stonefish, the butterfly cod has venomous spikes—the poles from which it flies its flags and banners as it parades through the water. A scratch from one of these can release a potent venom which, like that of the stonefish, is exceedingly painful. In fact, some authorities say the pain arising is out of all proportion to the apparent injury.

The venom is not likely to cause death, even in the extremely unlikely event that a swimmer is severely stung, but it can incapacitate for several days. One possible danger is a frightening fluctuation in temperature—a rapid rise and a sharp fall. This has been known to lead to collapse through cardiac failure and medical assistance should, of course, be sought.

There are several other venomous Australian fish generally known as scorpion or wasp fish. These are found in cooler, southern waters off the coast. There is the bullrout, the red rock cod, the fortescue and the goblin fish, all of which can give a painful wound from their venomous spines. None of these fish are deadly, but like their tropical cousins they are most unpleasant.

left: The gaudiest venomous fish in the sea is probably the butterfly cod, photographed here at the Green Island Marineland, near Cairns.

The stonefish.

Sea Snakes

The fish which have been discussed are all passive stingers—their venoms are weapons for defence only. Sea snakes on the other hand, are active stingers. They use their venom mechanism for hunting and killing.

Surprisingly little is known about sea snakes in the Australian region. In fact, it has probably been only in the last two or three years that we have begun to realize how common they are in tropical waters. I believe they will prove to be an increasing danger to man.

We are beginning to use our tropical seas more and more, both for commercial fishing and recreation. As this takes place, the chances of accidental contact with sea snakes will increase enormously. Already, I have spoken with prawn fishermen in the Gulf of Carpentaria and on the eastern coast of Queensland who tell of huge hauls of sea snakes. One boat, believing it had detected the classic 'boil' pattern on the water which reveals the presence of a shoal of prawns, ran its net around the disturbance and pulled in literally hundreds of sea snakes. The fishermen thought this was a mating phenomenon.

Individual sea snakes are very common in hauls of fish and prawns and they frequently slither through groups of fishermen working on the crowded deck. It seems to be only a matter of time before someone is bitten.

Ben Cropp, the diver and film-maker, is also convinced that at certain times of the year sea snakes are likely to menace, or even attack, divers coming into their territory. In June 1968, at Swain's Reef, on the outer part of the Barrier Reef, Ben, his wife Eva and an assistant, John Reynolds, were trying to photograph brown sea snakes.

The snakes were engaged in typical mating behaviour, swimming at one another, bunting and entwining. Sea snakes, like land snakes, usually try to flee when humans appear, but these did not react in this way. They refused to be frightened by lunges of spears and even the approach of an underwater camera. Instead they tried to entwine round the weapons and menace the diver.

One snake chased Reynolds more than thirty yards to the surface, although he kept kicking and hitting at it. Ben's tactic in this situation is to let the snake come at him, keep calm and then divert its attention to the flipper. As it comes at the flipper, he gives it a lusty whack, which usually seems, Ben says, to discourage it.

Other snake authorities disagree with this notion of aggression against humans. Eric Worrell, the snake authority at Gosford, says that no verified and purposeful attacks on human divers have been recorded. He considers that sea snakes' wary behaviour is comparable to that of land snakes.

Sea snakes are, of course, land reptiles which have taken to a watery environment and through evolution specialized accordingly. They generally have a flattened tail, like an eel's, for swimming. Sea snakes are all air breathers. They have a flap on each of their nostrils which allows them to come to the surface to breathe, and then closes as they swim underwater.

Most are helpless on land. The ventral plates, which are used by land snakes for motion, have almost disappeared in most sea snake species. However, fang structures and venom mechanisms are the same in both land and sea snakes.

One of the greatest contemporary authorities on sea snakes is the French scientist, Michel Barme, of the Institut Pasteur, in Paris. Barme has studied sea snakes in several areas of the Pacific, notably Vietnam, Malaysia and New Caledonia. He indicates that there are probably many more deaths from bites in Asian areas than is generally recognized.

'Sea snake venom is very toxic,' he wrote recently. 'Although the animals are not usually aggressive, there are so many on the shores of some countries that human victims are numerous.' Studies by other authorities show that about seventeen per cent of bites are fatal. Barme and British medical men in Malaysia note that most attacks occur among fishermen, usually in remote villages. The Asian fishermen are well aware of the danger, particularly as they fish in estuary areas of big river systems like the Mekong and Red River.

Bites from some Malayan sea snakes result in paralysis, including that of the eyelids, which close. Victims appear to go to sleep and die, even though fishermen who have recovered reluctantly told researchers that while they were supposedly unconscious, they were aware of what was going on round them and could hear and understand their friends talking.

The researchers found it most difficult to acquire clinical knowledge of these symptoms and of mortality rates, because villagers were just too scared to talk, believing that sea snakes owed allegiance to the King of the Snakes and the Genie of the Sea. If victims talked, they would arouse the ire of both these fearsome spirits.

However, one study of forty-eight fatal cases in Malaysia shows that twelve victims died within eight hours, twenty-three within twelve to twenty-four hours and the remainder within twenty-three days.

Sea snakes, like other marine creatures, are not limited to land boundaries. Hence, their distribution is judged more by the climatic and marine boundaries of what is called the 'Indo-Pacific Region'. Australia's northern coasts fall into this region, so the likelihood of a sea snake problem occurring in this area depends purely on the amount of human contact. If this is increasing—as it is at the moment—the risk is also increasing.

Australian authorities recognize at least ten species of sea snake found in Australian waters. These include *Enhydrina schistosa,* the venom of which is one of the most toxic known. Worrell warns that all species of sea snake found near Australia must be regarded as dangerous. His list, incidentally, does not include one species of *Laticauda* which Barme says is common in parts of New Caledonia. Barme notes that this type shows evidence of being aggres-

above: One of the rare pictures of an active sea snake. This brown sea snake shows a strong resemblance to land snakes in the shape of the head and strength of the body, but the flattened tail, used for swimming, shows the marine adaptation.

sive to man but also likes to climb out of the sea and bask on rocks and in vegetation along the beach. As New Caledonia is relatively close to Australia —and Barrier Reef conditions so similar to it—it seems most probable that this snake also exists off the Australian coast.

Sea snakes live on fish, which they hunt and kill with their venom. The snake swims up to a fish and bites it, often in mid-body. The venom quickly immobilizes the fish and some species appear to die within seconds. The snake does not relax its grip, but keeps its jaws

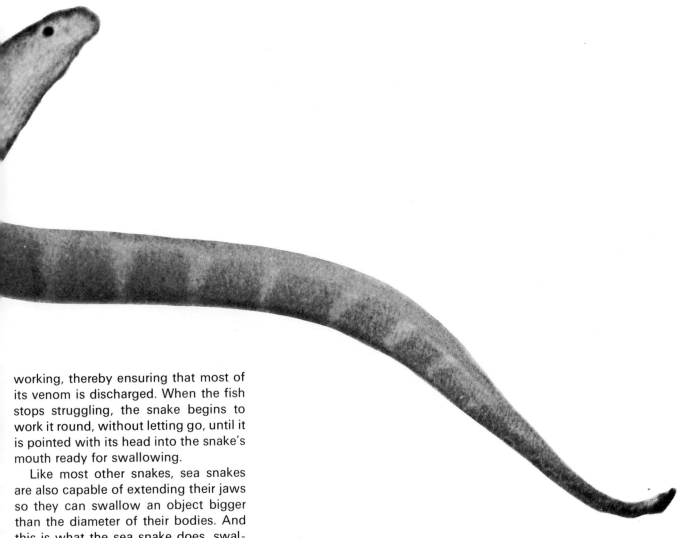

working, thereby ensuring that most of its venom is discharged. When the fish stops struggling, the snake begins to work it round, without letting go, until it is pointed with its head into the snake's mouth ready for swallowing.

Like most other snakes, sea snakes are also capable of extending their jaws so they can swallow an object bigger than the diameter of their bodies. And this is what the sea snake does, swallowing comparatively big fish, fins, spikes and all. In recorded cases of human bites, the snakes' refusal to let go has often been noted. Victims said the snakes 'nibbled' or 'chewed' at them. Often the venom fangs will break off and remain in the wound.

One difficulty when dealing with a sea snake attack is that the attack is not hard and vicious like that of land snakes like the taipan. Sometimes, it is hardly noticed and the snake itself is not seen in turbid and moving water, such as found in an estuary. Victims may collapse without their companions being aware of the attack.

The Malayan sea snake is such a problem that Australian scientists have developed an antivenene for its bite. But no antidotes exist for the bites of other types of sea snake found off the Australian coast. First aid, of course, is the standard snakebite procedure of tourniquet, washing of the wound and also removing as much venom as possible by sucking. Medical attention should be sought as quickly as possible. In the case of a bite, also try to secure the snake for identification.

above: A closer view of the brown sea snake.

THE TAIPAN

If the lion is king of the beasts, then surely the Australian taipan must have a claim to be king of the snakes.

The taipan is our biggest and most venomous snake. He is also regarded as one of the fastest and the most intelligent. And in today's man-dominated world, the taipan is passing the ultimate test—he is holding his own against man's intrusion into his country, our tropical north and the inland, and is maintaining his numbers.

To prepare material for this book, I travelled over eastern Australia from Cape York to Melbourne and interviewed many of our leading naturalists and scientists in this field. All agreed in their admiration for the taipan, even the handlers who have been bitten and who nearly died from its bite.

In world literature, the rattlesnake, the cobra, the krait, the viper and the African mamba top the horror ratings. Generally, the king cobra of India and South East Asia is regarded as the most fearsome of all. But these snakes owe much of their fame to first-class public relations officers. Rudyard Kipling and many others wrote about the cobra and built up its reputation, which was already based on the religions and legends of Indian civilization. But who has there been to write like this about the taipan and other Australian snakes? Authorities like Worrell and Harold Cogger have been cool and factual in their approach, but even so their admiration for the taipan comes through.

The cool facts show without any doubt that in one measure of deadliness, the amount and potency of venom, the famous snakes of America, Africa and Asia are strictly small time compared to Australian snakes. In particular, the taipan is outstanding. Although its venom is slightly less potent than that of some species of tiger snake, its rival in Australian snake legends, it carries almost four times as much. In an average milking, the taipan will yield enough venom to give 120 milligrams dry weight. The tiger will give thirty-five milligrams.

Eric Worrell says that the taipan's stock of venom is capable (if gruesomely injected), of killing 23,500 laboratory mice. The biggest tiger could kill 8,800; the mainland tiger 5,800 and

the death adder 2,300. On top of this deadliness, the taipan is clever, fast and very angry when provoked.

Our taipan belongs to northern Australia and to Papua and New Guinea. It has been reported as far south as the 'corners' region inland, where Queensland, South Australia and New South Wales meet, and on the coast as far south as Brisbane. The biggest specimen ever recorded was eleven feet long (compare this with the fourteen feet of India's King Cobra) although eight feet would be regarded normally as big and six feet a good average.

You can see the taipan at most Australian nature reserves or zoos and it is worth having a close look at it. One of

the best and most educational places is Eric Worrell's Australian Reptile Park near Gosford, where you can also see taipans 'milked' for venom research. Worrell is probably Australia's foremost snake expert and is the published authority on most species.

Most Australian taipans you see are a dark brown with characteristic yellow-brown eyes but they range between light olive brown to dark chestnut or russet brown. Their bellies are lighter, often a creamy yellow in front and white behind. This is freckled with a reddish pink and in life the belly surface is overlaid with an iridescent mother of pearl bloom. They are easily mistaken for brown snakes. But to an expert, the graceful shape, particularly the slender front body and long head, is distinctive.

The taipan is a well developed, specialized and highly lethal killer. It preys on small mammals, typically rats, tracking them down with its keen senses of sight and smell, immobilizing them instantly with its venomous bite and swallowing them whole. Cairns naturalist Garry Zillfleisch reports instances where they have eaten creatures as big as bandicoots.

When white settlement started in the north, the first arrivals found that the Aboriginals already knew a lot about the taipan and held it in dread. Over the years, it had been responsible for many

deaths among them. In nearly every instance, the bite was fatal.

To learn about taipans, I went to the Cairns area where they are relatively common, but seldom seen, because the taipan is a shy snake and does not deserve the aggressive reputation with which he has been branded. Although all the people I spoke to painted this picture of the shy and retiring taipan, I did not really believe it until I went out looking for specimens with Mossman snake-catcher Fred Rossignoli. He chose the typical country liked by the snake, with blady-grass, fallen trees, warm rocks and old farm buildings on the tablelands, inland from the coast.

Fred catches taipans for sale either to private collectors or to local zoos and expects to get between $6 and $8 a foot for them. He relies on a snake intelligence system based on local tip-offs. He also maintains good relations with farmers, who usually see taipans during the course of their daily farm rounds. The farmers are only too glad to have a taipan removed if they can find someone like Fred willing to do it at no cost and risk to themselves.

Fred's method is to chase a taipan and grab it by the tail, playing it like a trout until it is exhausted. He refuses to use the traditional forked stick, saying the taipan threshes around so vigorously that it is likely to damage itself internally. When the snake is exhausted, he grabs it behind the head and drops it into his bag.

We spent all day out, covering the ground at a fairly fast trot and visiting areas where taipans had been frequently and recently seen. But we did not see any. The probable explanation was that they heard us coming and had slid away.

The taipan does, however, have a reputation for getting itself into a rage and striking in a frenzy. In observed cases, this behaviour has followed man's deliberately annoying a taipan, for instance by attempting to kill it with a stick. 'Taipans, like all snakes, are very wary of humans,' Garry Zillfleisch, who runs Hartley's Creek Fauna Reserve, told me. 'Otherwise there'd be a lot of people bitten, and there'd be nobody left in north Queensland if they chased us as much as people have been led to believe.

'However, it can be a different story if they are enraged. There have been good examples of a snake in anger turning round and attacking tractors and things like that. Recently, a tourist coach going to Cooktown passed by a taipan just starting to cross the road. The snake took it as an aggressive act and struck at the wheels of the bus as it went past. The people could see the venom on the tyres when they stopped. But this is clearly a defensive attack.

'Taipans are the most intelligent of all the snakes and the easiest provoked into an attack if they are cornered. They don't muck around....But if when they are cornered, you take the initiative and

above left: A taipan on sandy soil. Normally this dangerous snake is found in open tropical bush country in a habitat of grass and fallen trees or the environs of man's farms and houses. However, it has become established over much of eastern Australia, including the inland semi-desert lands.

retreat you will find they retreat also—this I'll guarantee.'

Despite this hair-trigger relationship, taipans and man appear to be moving closer together in the north. The taipan has developed into an efficient and fast rat killer. He is capable of going down a rat hole and striking repeatedly (spinning out his venom supply while he does so) until every rat in the hole is dead. There is a machine-like precision in this. The taipan tracks on scent and strikes at movement. The combination stacks the odds against rats. But as rats in vast numbers have followed man, particularly into an environment of farms and canefields, taipans have found conditions most favourable for them as well.

'The food value of the cane is so high that it attracts rats in hordes,' Zillfleisch went on. 'You get a lot of snakes coming in.' 'The taipan must be doing a pretty good rat control job around here then,' I remarked.

'My word,' Zillfleisch agreed. But then he quickly went on: 'Even with the good point of their killing rats, the danger to man is so pronounced that I'm all for removing them from anywhere where there's likely to be people. I appreciate the balance of nature, but commonsense must prevail.

'If I saw a taipan around here, I would try to kill it. The difference is that if you stand on another snake like the red-bellied black you might get bitten. If you stand on a taipan you will be bitten. And if there's no help around, you'll probably die.'

One of the first people in the north to make the taipan danger known to the nation as a whole was Tom Briggs, now superintendent of the Cairns Ambulance. A lifetime of work has made him aware of the avoidable hazards that venomous animals represent.

In 1950 he presented a paper to a State ambulance conference in Cairns which assembled what was then known about the taipan. Briggs presented the scientific description, first published by the Zoological Society of London in 1933 and then added to this his own observations and the knowledge that he

right: Sydney snake handler John Cann displays a taipan, the most dangerous of Australia's venomous snakes.

had gleaned in ambulance work.

'It is undoubtedly the biggest and probably the most dangerous venomous snake found in Australia,' he said. 'The natives hold the taipan in great dread and it appears to have been responsible for many deaths among them.

'When annoyed the taipan does not flatten its body as do most Australian snakes. It depresses its sides so that the vertebral column stands up like a keel.

'It also has a curious habit when about to attack of raising one of two coils of its body for several inches clear of the ground, its head slightly raised and flattened to such an extent that all the angles of the jaw protrude. At the same time it erects its tail in the air and waves it to and fro. Its behaviour gives it a sinister appearance. After remaining in this attitude for some seconds, it strikes suddenly and with extreme rapidity.

'When biting, the taipan does not seize and "chew" its victim as does, for example, the powerful and aggressive king brown (or mulga) snake. It snaps three or four times in succession so that there is no possibility of its victim escaping any of the bites. It then takes hold, snapping again at intervals. Observation of the biting mechanism and venom yields show that at the first two or three snap bites, the greater part of the venom is expressed.

'Of all the victims known to have been bitten by this reptile, only one recovered. And in this case, there was no positive proof of the identity of the snake although it was claimed to have been a taipan.'

Giving two fatal case histories, Mr Briggs referred to an incident in 1938 where a meat inspector, a Mr Sibley, was bitten near Mareeba. The bite went through khaki trousers and socks. Sibley's companion ran for help and when he returned only minutes later he found the victim's arms and legs had become paralysed. By the time the rest of the party arrived, he was going blind. When an ambulance met the party two hours later, the patient was going black. He was admitted to hospital five hours

left: The snake-milking technique. The snake's fangs are pressed against a diaphragm over a container and the venom is expelled.

after the bite and died an hour later, conscious but unable to speak.

The other case was that of a farmer at Mossman who blamed a taipan living in the hollow of an old mango tree on the property for stock losses. He went to kill it with a hoe.

'Unfortunately, the taipan proved too fast for Mr Pringle and his hoe,' Mr Briggs noted in his paper. 'He was bitten; ran to the house which was situated on a nearby hill and died almost immediately.'

The man who survived what was thought to be a taipan bite was a Mr F. V. Hardwick, bitten once on the hand by a snake which was identified as a six-foot taipan, but which escaped. A companion gave him first aid, including a tourniquet and took him to hospital immediately. Even so, he was ill for seven weeks, twelve days of this time in a most serious condition. Nine months later the wound was still septic and Mr Hardwick still had not regained his senses of taste and smell.

Growing awareness of the danger of the taipan and the work of people like Eric Worrell, who captured specimens, studied them and worked out a milking procedure to get venom, allowed the Commonwealth Serum Laboratories to prepare an antivenene in 1955. Almost immediately, the antidote began saving lives.

Tom Briggs found himself recording one of the first heartening case histories. The victim was then aged ten, a schoolboy called Bruce Stringer, who was playing on the hillside near the school when he was bitten on the outer side of his right knee.

'I think the lad contributed in a great measure to his own recovery by having the presence of mind to grasp and hold on to the raised flesh firmly in the vicinity of the bite,' Mr Briggs noted.

He hobbled for 200 yards to his headmaster, who immediately applied a rubber ligature and scarified the wound. Although the tourniquet was in place within three minutes of the bite, the boy had started to complain about lack of vision. A few minutes later he was unconscious. Within twenty-five minutes, the patient was in Cairns Hospital. He was given a shot of tiger snake antivenene and eventually (after temporary

releases), the ligature was taken off. The boy's condition remained good until six o'clock the next morning after he had been kept awake all night.

He then had difficulty in opening his eyes because of paralysis of the eyelids; he started vomiting and suffered abdominal pains. Through the day, Bruce's condition deteriorated still more and in the afternoon the hospital's medical superintendent decided to give him the still experimental taipan antivenene.

'A dramatic and unmistakable improvement took place within half an hour,' Mr Briggs reported. 'At this stage when told people were inquiring how he was, Bruce replied: "You can tell them I'm not dead yet."' By late afternoon he had moved out of danger and although some symptoms persisted, within two days he was almost back to normal.

The Bruce Stringer case attracted great interest through north Queensland, partly because of the boy's quick thinking in the initial emergency but later because his successful survival meant that a new measure of safety was available to people in taipan areas. What made the incident even more significant was that some time previously there had been a fatal taipan bite in the same area. The victim was Mr Keith Budden, of Sydney, described as a professional snake catcher.

Another person saved by the new antivenene was an ecologist, Mr Ken Slater, now of Canberra, who was bitten while studying taipans in Port Moresby. But even with the antivenene, taipan bites are a serious matter, particularly if the victim, because of possible allergic reaction, is unable to accept the antidote. One such victim was Mr Athol Comptom, who now works for Eric Worrell at Gosford. Comptom, when bitten, came so close to death his heart twice stopped beating.

If you look at a map of taipan distribution in Australia, you will see a long tongue coming down the western Queensland border—and this previously unknown taipan area was discovered because of Comptom's experience. It was in this Corners area that Comptom picked up what he thought was a brown snake and found he had a taipan. It bit him on the thumb.

'I applied a tourniquet and used

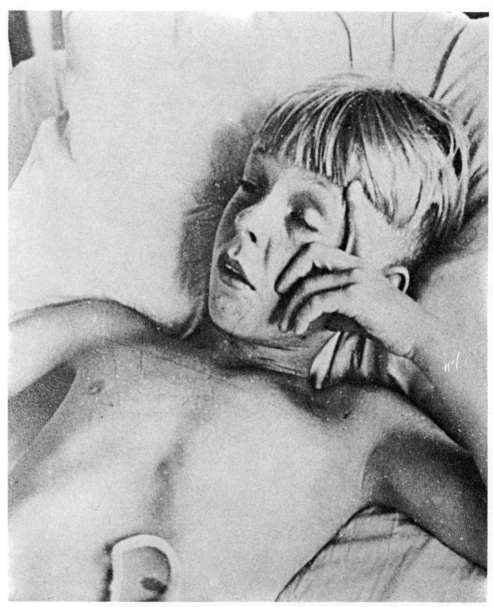

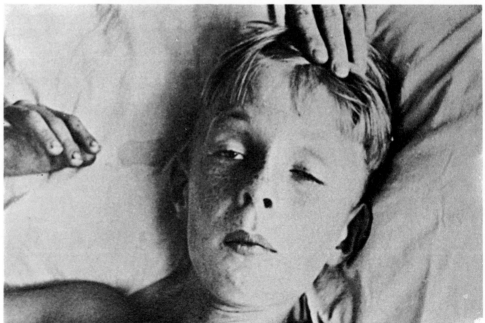

The first victim to recover from a taipan bite was Bruce Stringer of Cairns, who was bitten in 1955. The two photographs on this page display symptoms of the bite which included facial paralysis and lack of co-ordination of the eyes.

incisions,' Comptom told me. We had met, of all places, on the front steps of the Lodge at Karumba in the heart of Queensland's Gulf country. Comptom, a collector and a wanderer by nature, had come up to the Gulf from Sydney in a Landrover convoy with a party of travellers, to share with them some of his knowledge of and love for the Australian outback.

Comptom's action in incising the wound, incidentally, is an old bushman's remedy. The idea is to wash out the venom and bleed out any that may have penetrated. Modern practice now is not to cut the area of the wound.

Comptom sat back on his heels in the shade and went on with his story, which is one of the best-documented taipan bite incidents known and which has been reported as a case history in key medical journals.

'In about fifteen minutes I started to feel the first effects of the bite,' he said. 'This was mainly lack of judgment in distance. There was no other feeling of being sick or pain. I got in a car and started driving for help and found I couldn't judge corners.

'We made it to a station about twenty miles away with the idea of using their flying doctor radio set. But this was broken down, so I had to rig my portable radio. I couldn't complete the driving, by the way. I had to hand over to one of the chaps with me.

'By the time I got on air my speech had thickened and I was feeling slightly drunk. My eyes had become bloodshot, I was quite calm. I had decided by this time from the effects and because a doctor was so far away—I was 400 miles from the base at Broken Hill—that there was only going to be a very slim chance of getting over this one.

'By this time, I was just about due to collapse. There was still no pain but I couldn't sit up, so I handed the radio over to one of the chaps with me. My friends picked me up then all my muscles went. I lost control of my legs, my bowels—the lot. I could still think, but I couldn't co-ordinate.

'From then on I started to lose consciousness. I felt well, which is not a good sign. This indicates that there is little your body can do to fight the venom.

'This chap who was working the radio for me kept notes. The doctor told him to take my temperature and the first reading on the case notes was that my temperature was too low to register on the thermometer. It gradually came up, however. They gave me an aspirin or something.

'Occasionally I was conscious and felt well. I found my vision had doubled —one picture on top of the other, vertically. I was also vomiting. I can remember the doctor arriving. He got a needle out and I said: "Now, I can't take antivenene. I'm allergic to horse serum."'

'I remember him saying: "Well, you're a big help." And I can remember other vague sorts of things. I can't remember the trip to Broken Hill at all. On the flight my heart stopped and they revived me. It stopped again in the hospital in Broken Hill. I was unconscious all this time. I was flown from there to Adelaide—it was a Friday night. I became conscious again on Monday, about midday.'

Compton made almost a complete recovery and is still active, working around snakes including the pickled body of the one that nearly killed him.

'There are after effects,' he told me, adding regretfully: 'I have no sensations of either smell or taste. I can't drink alcohol like I used to either.'

Worrell, with his intimate experience of Australian taipans, does however concede that it has a deadlier cousin. This is the Papuan taipan, minutely described by Ken Slater who studied it in Port Moresby. Instead of the brown tones of the mainland variety, Papuan taipans are grey to black with an orange to vermilion stripe down the back. This becomes most conspicuous when the snake dilates its body, for instance when aroused. The belly is creamy with orange flecks. While generally it has all the elite qualities of the Australian taipan, the venom of the Papuan taipan is probably slightly more potent.

When you next go to a reptile park, have a good look at the taipan— Papuan or Australian—and admire him as king of the snakes. Treat him with respect too, if you are out in the bush. Co-existence is the secret to survival for both of you.

SNAKES

Of the world's 2,500 snake species, Australia has some 140. There are nine major families of 'serpents'—the translation of the scientific name of the sub-order which embraces the snake family. Of these, three are found in Australia. One group embraces the harmless blind snakes, the second the non-venomous pythons and boas, including the colourful Australian carpet and diamond snakes (which make good pets, if you are that way inclined) and the third, the Colubridae, contains the venomous snakes. Of these, possibly twenty Australian species are dangerous although the number of known deadly ones is likely to be closer to a dozen.

There are no venomous lizards in Australia, contrary to popular belief. By and large, this means if a reptile has legs it is harmless and should not be killed in terror—more so since many lizards double up as efficient predators on young venomous snakes. There are, however, a few lizards which are legless. To the lay eye, these are difficult to distinguish from snakes. Some, however, have vestiges of legs while all have rigidly hinged jaws, just as humans do. Snake jaws are hinged in an elastic fashion so they can expand and allow the snake to swallow something as big as—or sometimes even bigger than—its own body.

Although most of our deadly snakes have adapted themselves to living in the new environment which man, with his settlement, agriculture and roads has created, few Australians ever see them in the wild state. The story of a Melbourne research group that wanted to capture some copperheads shows why this happens. They went to a farmer and asked if they could search suitable country on his property. 'Go ahead,' the farmer said. 'But you won't see any. I haven't seen a snake down that way for twenty years.' The group caught something like thirty in an afternoon.

The reason is that all snakes are shy animals. They go out of their way, by and large, to avoid humans. Occasionally they will seem to be aggressive, but this is usually only when the human has got the snake cornered or aroused, or when the human is between the snake and the place to which he wants to escape.

Most estimates say that about seventy or eighty per cent of all snake 'attacks' take place when a human is, in fact, attacking a snake. Nearly all the rest are completely accidental, for instance stepping on a snake in the bush. Despite the stories you hear, the evidence is clearly that if you see a snake and obey your instinct to run away, the snake will do the same. Dignity may be a bit ruffled, but this way nobody gets hurt.

A dispassionate look at the snake from a physical point of view will show how, in fact, the odds in any such encounter are stacked against him. Instinctively, the snake realizes this so he does his best to avoid trouble. As I have said earlier, the snake has not evolved to prey on people.

Our snakes are highly specialized animals. They are carnivorous, but most of them eat insects and small creatures like frogs and lizards. Some of the venomous ones, the taipan for instance, prey on small mammals. They have no arms or legs. They have no ears. Their only sense of hearing comes through an internal arrangement, not nearly as efficient as other more highly-developed animal hearing systems, for instance the arrangement which man and most mammals have. Snakes' hearing allows them to pick up little more than low-frequency vibrations through the ground. One of these would be the danger signal of man's tread.

Their short-range vision is most acute. There seems to be a marked differentiation between day and night-hunting snakes. The former have big round pupils, the latter vertical ones.

The most highly-developed sense in snakes is that of smell. Their normal sense of smell is good, but they back this up with a method of 'tasting' the air—the significance of the flicking forked tongue. The tongue picks up particles in the air and transfers these back to pits in the roof of the mouth called 'Jacobson's organs'. This heightens snakes' ability to detect prey and dangers.

Snakes can move around fairly well, although it is a most laborious process. Their long, sinuous structure is built up round something like 200 ribs, which have muscles attached to them. These in turn can work the hard shields attached to the lower part of their bodies. To

below: A tiger snake at Eric Worrell's Australian Reptile Park. In this specimen the stripes are almost indiscernible, and as this frequently occurs tiger snakes can be confused with black or brown snakes.
bottom: David Fleay with phials of venom produced from milking snakes at his fauna reserve at Burleigh Heads, Queensland.

move, snakes throw their bodies ahead in a series of curves, getting a grip on the surface with the edges of the shields, which the muscles work in a fascinating, rippling style. Their sinuous bodies allow them to move easily through grass and bush, or even underground, in search of food.

Most snakes can move along at a speed about the same as a man's brisk walking pace. There is no indication that, as the stories suggest, they can out-distance a galloping horse. Furthermore, they have to get a grip on the surface to be able to get along at all. On a smooth surface, they are just about helpless and merely writhe around.

To prey on other animals, as they have no claws or legs, their only two weapons are the bite and the ability to grip with the whole body. The venomous snakes have developed the biting weapon; the constrictors the powerful body. You will, however, find venomous snakes that grip with their bodies and constrictors that bite. In the latter event, however, the bite is not venomous and while it can be a nasty gash which turns septic (like a dog's bite, for instance)

you will not keel over and die from its effects.

There are two major sorts of venomous snakes. One type has its fangs at the rear. These fangs are merely grooved, so that the venom runs down a gutter into the wound. The major Australian example of this type is the brown tree snake, found mainly in the north, which because of its big eyes has the lovely popular name of 'doll's eyes', in some areas. To get a venomous bite from one of these snakes, you would almost have to stick your finger into its mouth and allow it to chew you. For this reason, it cannot be considered dangerous.

The front-fanged snakes are, however, a somewhat different proposition. The fangs are like hypodermic needles, with a tube down the length of the tooth leading from the venom glands so that when the snake strikes, its fangs pierce the flesh and inject the venom deep into the flesh of the victim. If a tiger snake or taipan bites by ill-chance right into a vein, the action of its venom will be rapid.

To consider how a front-fanged venomous snake uses its bite and

below: One variation of the deadly tiger snake. This snake has many forms and colours but is generally distinguishable by bold stripes. This picture was taken at the Australian Reptile Park, Gosford, where Eric Worrell has assembled one of the nation's best snake collections in surroundings which are natural and at the same time permit amateurs to study snakes in safety.

venom, look once more at its problems. It must first track its prey or lie in wait for it. It does this with its augmented sense of smell and its short-range vision. It then has to bite and immobilize it and swallow it whole. The snake has no limbs and claws to dismember its food into bite-sized chunks. This is where the venom is such a useful weapon. When a front-fanged snake bites, it hangs on until venom is injected into its victim or, like the taipan, it might strike hard three or four times. The venom quickly takes effect on a small creature.

Venom has evolved from the snake's saliva. So not only does it immobilize the prey, it also begins the digestive process. This can even take the form of breaking down tissue inside the animal. The snake then turns the prey around so it can swallow it head first. And this is where the elastic jaw hinge comes in handy.

Even when the snake has swallowed its food, its problems are not over. It must call up powerful, fast-acting digestive juices to start breaking down the food and these operate only when the snake's body temperature is high enough. The snake is a 'cold-blooded' creature, so that this temperature depends on the outside temperature. In suddenly cool conditions a snake which is digesting its prey faces the danger that the food will ferment and the snake itself die of food poisoning. Its venom and digestive juices play a major role in inhibiting fermentation.

Snake venom is consequently a complex biological fluid which, over the whole range, can have a number of effects on human victims. Several of these effects may be present in the one type of venom. Certainly, the characteristic of each type of snake venom is different. This is why it is important to identify the snake as accurately as possible in the case of snakebite so that correct medical treatment and antidotes can be given.

The Commonwealth Serum Laboratories lists four main venom constituents. The predominant toxin present in any particular snake's venom will determine the effects on the victim.

1. **Neurotoxins:** These are poisons which block communication between the nerve ends and muscles. This leads

to paralysis. Neurotoxins are the most common element in most Australian snake venoms, and in other venoms as well.

2. **Haemorrhagin**: This is an enzyme which breaks down tissue, particularly blood vessels and internal organs.

3. **Haemolysin**: This destroys red blood cells. It is commonly present in Australian venoms, but particularly so in the black snake and copperhead. However, while contributory, it is not a major cause of fatalities.

4. **Thrombase**: This is a blood coagulant, also present in most Australian venoms. It could be the killer, according to some authorities, when the venom is injected into a major artery.

All these constituents play an important part in the work for which each venom has been evolved, the immobilization of a particular prey and the preparation of it as food. As man is not on the menu for any snake, the venom is obviously used against humans in its secondary role—that of defence. What happens, then, in a typical case of snakebite?

Firstly, there is a wound, sometimes small but often very obvious. Each snake has a distinctive wound. The taipan, as mentioned, strikes hard and several times. The tiger snake on the other hand grabs hold and 'chews'. Usually there are two puncture wounds in each bite, but there can be more because snakes develop a second set of fangs in reserve in case the first pair gets broken. If the skin area has been broken several times, by either the snake's biting action or by the tearing caused by pulling the snake off, it is sometimes hard to pick up the actual punctures. On the other hand, these may sometimes bleed, perhaps for some days. A venomous bite causes little reaction in the area of the bite, however, while a python or similar non-venomous constricting snake will leave a series of wounds corresponding to a healthy set of teeth.

Secondly, the specific effects of a venomous bite begin to appear, often fairly quickly as seen in the taipan case histories. A tourniquet is a good delaying measure, but it will not indefinitely prevent the venom escaping from the area. Suction of the wound and washing to remove venom is, however, strongly recommended. Incision is now frowned on, as is the use of Condy's crystals. The main aim is to minimize the amount of venom actually affecting the victim and to delay its onset so medical attention—and particularly an antivenene antidote—can be secured.

Typical symptoms are drowsiness, headache, nausea, then vomiting, sweating, diarrhoea, faintness, faults in vision and eventually loss of consciousness. An advanced effect, resulting from tissue breakdown and loss of blood internally, can be the passing of red or black urine. This symptom, incidentally, has been noticed by French researchers at the Institut Pasteur in Paris to result from sea snake bites also but has been found to have other and more complex cellular causes than mere tissue destruction.

The medical effects of snake bite are well documented and available from authorities like the Commonwealth Serum Laboratories (C.S.L.). Doctors called on to treat snakebite victims, even though the snake itself has not been captured, can assemble evidence on the identity of the 'attacker' through the symptoms which develop. They can also, of course, make an intelligent guess by being aware of what dangerous snakes inhabit their region and the nature of the country where the incident occurred.

I find it almost incredible that there are so few snakebites in Australia. Nowadays, fatalities are so rare that they are reported widely as major news. This happens despite the quite heavy population densities in areas where there are many venomous snakes. The reasons, I believe, are firstly the shyness of snakes, then the commonsense precautions most Australians take. After this we have the availability of fast transport to take victims to hospitals where they can be treated (as in the Compton case). Finally, there is the magnificent work that our medical scientists have carried out in developing antivenenes.

It is only in the last twenty years or less that the latter two factors have played a major part. They have saved many lives. But the balance between safety and danger is very delicate in Australia. The figures of only four or five deaths a year here, compared with

pages 72-73—
left: The copperhead, a deadly species particularly common in Victoria, but very shy and wary of humans as a rule.
centre: Another variation in tiger snake appearance.
right: A black and a brown snake.

opposite: Swampy surroundings show off the sheen of the glossy black snake.

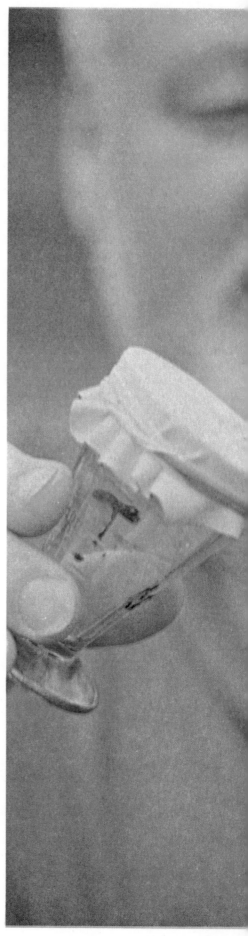

left: Milking a tiger snake. First expert Eric Worrell snares the snake and grasps it behind the head where it cannot strike him but he can force its mouth open exposing the long venomous fangs. . . .

below: The snake's head is then pressed on to a diaphragm so that its fangs pierce the skin and shoot their venom into the glass container.

top: The red-bellied black snake.

above: Another unusually-marked tiger snake. In this specimen the bands are barely visible.

35,000 in Asia and about 5,000 in South America, show this. Occasionally, when the balance gets upset in Australia, the number of bites increases greatly. About 1952, for instance, there was flooding in Melbourne and the rising waters drove snakes into inhabited areas. There were fifty-two snakebite cases recorded in that summer in and around Melbourne.

However, each Australian State has its quota of venomous snakes and they are all likely to be encountered by anyone walking through the area in which they live. Victoria's dangerous snakes are tiger snakes, brown snakes, copperheads and red-bellied black snakes, all of which are found in areas where there is also the greatest population. The 'king brown' or mulga snake, which is really a sort of black snake, is also likely to be encountered in the north-western section around the Murray Valley. So far there are no records of taipans in Victoria, but the identification of this deadly snake in the Murray system would not surprise naturalists.

Tasmania has only the tiger snake and the copperhead. There is, however, a huge version of the tiger snake in the Bass Strait islands and this should be treated with the greatest respect.

The five venomous snakes of Victoria —the tiger, brown, copperhead, red-bellied black and mulga snakes—are also found in New South Wales in various areas. The death adder is also present in drier areas and there have been reports of taipans in the Darling area which, so far, have not been identified. The taipan is, however, present in northern coastal regions.

Queensland has what the C.S.L. terms 'the venomous seven' with the exception of the copperhead. South Australia's more settled regions lack the taipan (although it is found in the desert) but it does have two brown snakes, the gwardar and the collared. A grey-bellied snake, also a member of the brown snake family has been discovered in small numbers and is dangerous although the likelihood of anyone being bitten is remote.

A desert death adder joins the list for the Northern Territory and central Australia as well as a whip snake, known as the spotted-headed snake. This also is a

relative of the brown snake. The gwardar in drier areas and the taipan in the north are the main dangers.

Western Australia shares the gwardar and the mulga snakes with the east and the desert death adder with the centre. It has, however, developed what is classified as its own species of tiger snake and brown snake the latter known as the dugite. All are closely related to their cousins in the east so appropriate antivenenes can be used to treat bites.

New Guinea's claim to snake fame is the Papuan black snake, a huge version of the black family, which is closely related to the mulga snake. This causes more deaths than any other. As noted, the Papuan taipan probably shades even the mainland version in deadliness. The death adder is present in some highland valleys—to such an extent that certain areas were until recently no-man's lands.

While these are Australia's major deadly snakes, it is worth noting that there are one or two other rarer specimens which have been known to kill, such as the small Clarence River snake of New South Wales. The individual species will be discussed in more detail in the next chapter.

Listing dangerous snakes like this is quite frightening. It makes it seem as if they are lurking beneath every log, or coiled up behind every bush. In fact, most of us will never see a dangerous snake in its natural state. Although I have been out in the bush and scrub much more than most people—and in fact have gone out deliberately looking for taipans and others—the only wild venomous snake I have seen in recent years was a wandering brown snake which slithered past the window of my home. We were sitting down having lunch at the time. Had we been outside making our usual commotion and betraying our presence in other ways, the chances are that the brown snake would have avoided the area completely. The chances also are that he lives in the bushland and rocks we have surrounding our home—and I have never seen him since.

I have, however, seen many other snakes, most of them carpet and diamond snakes in Queensland—two varieties which do only good and which many people like to have around their home like a cat to keep rats and mice away.

This experience supports the expert opinion that while we need to be wary and take obvious precautions, we can remember that only about a dozen species are likely to be dangerous. Of these, only one or two are likely to be found in a specific area. These we should be able to recognize by making ourselves familiar with their appearance in a reptile park.

If you come across a dangerous snake in the open, you should give it a wide berth and leave plenty of room for it to retreat as well. If, however, it is in an area where it may endanger people, particularly children, the best thing to do is to get an expert in to catch it or kill it. Unless you are experienced and have plenty of room in which to move, the experts do not advise going after it yourself. There are always people like Fred Rossignoli around who are only too happy to catch it for you free of charge.

Garry Zillfleisch, of Hartley's Creek, is one person who is convinced that if people left snakes alone there would be almost no bites in this country. But, he told me, the average Australian just cannot do this.

'Your instinct, just like the snake's, is to turn and run,' he said. 'But we don't listen to our instincts. We think if we get that snake it's something to brag about, something to talk about down at the pub, so we get a stick and try to kill it.

'Perhaps you might be between the snake and his escape and get him good and mad so he has a go at you. And that's how every snake attack story I've heard about has started.'

However good this advice may be, few Australians seem likely to act on it in the heat of the moment. Hopefully, we can learn to recognize the dangerous snakes and leave the others unharmed. And this is the purpose of the next chapter.

left: two black snakes.

left: A deadly brown snake poised to strike.

THE DEADLY EIGHT

In this chapter, my aim is to list the few dangerous snakes in Australia and Papua-New Guinea. The choice is a subjective one. It does not claim to be by any means complete and it also does not intend to compete with full scientific descriptions. Treat this chapter as a guide only. If you want to learn more about snakes, turn to the section which lists some of the references that are available. If, however, you are a bushwalker and would like to recognize venomous snakes, buy a copy of one of the better guides. The one I prefer is Eric Worrell's *Dangerous Snakes of Australia and New Guinea,* which at time of writing was in reprint of its fifth edition. Worrell is constantly updating this work.

From the medical point of view, the best guide is one made available by the Commonwealth Serum Laboratories to the medical profession, supplemented by the individual brochures on antivenenes. This chapter is based mainly on the C.S.L. selection, which in turn is based on their experience in snakebite research and supplying antidotes over many years. However, it will also be supplemented by my own interviews and reading from many sources.

The system used is to group the snakes into major types and then deal under these headings with the different species where necessary. Scientific names are listed in the index at the end of the book.

left: The Commonwealth Serum Laboratories near Melbourne where much of Australia's venom research is carried out and where antivenenes are produced. The C.S.L. is a world leader in both these fields.

page 84: A tiger snake. The venom of this snake is probably the deadliest in the world, although the snake's fangs do not have the venom capacity of the taipan. However, as tiger snakes are common close to major centres of population in Australia, they have in the past accounted for a big proportion of snakebite casualties.

Tiger Snakes

Next to the taipan, the tiger snake family is the most dangerous group of snakes in Australia. The venom of some varieties is even more potent than that of the taipan, while others again are almost as big in size.

What makes the tiger snake potentially so dangerous is its distribution, which is closely parallel to the heaviest human settlement in Australia. Tiger snakes are found from just north of the Queensland border, in the Brisbane region, right across the south-eastern corner of Australia into the Adelaide and Gulf region of South Australia. They are also found in the coastal part of southern Western Australia, from Perth around the coast to Albany and beyond. Tiger snakes are also general in Tasmania.

The most common type of tiger snake is distributed right through this zone, except for the Western Australian section. Colours vary widely from yellowish to orange, brown or black. The tiger snakes get their name from the aggressive stripes found on many specimens, but some members of the family do not have them. In shape the snakes are thick and flatten out distinctively when angry and about to strike. Commonly, they are four feet to four feet six inches in length. They hunt mainly by day, but on warm summer nights they are also likely to be out and about. Contrary to popular belief, by and large the tiger snake is inoffensive and will avoid contact. As Worrell points out in one of his books, there are thousands of them in some parts of the Murray Valley and no cases of snakebite have been reported from these areas.

The western tiger snake, the Western Australian version, is very similar but is differentiated as a separate variety. It is steel blue to brown in colour, with narrow, yellowish cross-bands. Venom properties, while still being investigated, can be assumed to be similar to the common tiger snake of the eastern States.

Another tiger snake, first described as a separate species but now regarded as being more probably a variety, comes from the Spencer's Gulf area of South Australia. This is known as the peninsula tiger snake. Its claim to notoriety is that it has the world's most potent venom. However, authorities say the snake is comparatively rare. Its colour is jet black with a greyish belly. The young have light grey bands, and the adult length is usually under five feet.

The islands of Bass Strait house the biggest tiger snakes of them all—and also one of the strangest snake stories in Australia. The snakes are recognized as belonging to a separate species—and grow to eight feet in length. These are Chappell Island tiger snakes, described and named by Worrell, from Chappell Island and Badger Island in the Furneaux group.

On these islands they share burrows with mutton birds, the shearwater chickens, which form the basis of an extensive industry. Despite the danger, mutton bird hunters put their hands into the burrows and pull out the chickens during the brief season each year. And, of course, many have been bitten over the years. Worrell, who has studied these snakes in some detail, writes that he believes the timid snakes hide behind the fat chicks when the hunters rifle the burrows. Despite this, there were two bites while he was on the island, one of which was serious. He believes the big snakes feast on mutton bird chicks for a few weeks of the year, store fat and live on it for the rest of the time.

While the arrangement seems to be a rather one-way deal, Worrell points out that paradoxically the snakes also provide a degree of protection. Without them, introduced rats would have wiped out the helpless chicks in short order.

The remaining species of tiger snake is Krefft's, named after a herpetologist who first described it in the nineteenth century. This is a rare species, less than three feet in length and also black, which lives in the Flinders Ranges area of South Australia.

Tiger snake venom, while carried in only about one-quarter the volume of that of the taipan, attacks the nervous system, breaks down tissues and also coagulates the blood. The tiger fastens on to the victim and 'chews', forcing his venom out. Before the development of an antivenene, almost half the known victims died.

Most bites occur during wet seasons,

when rivers and lakes flood and the snakes are driven closer to habitation. The snakes are also likely to take up residence in farm buildings where feed is stored and haystacks kept, because these attract rats and mice on which they can prey. From time to time, farmers and station owners have made efforts to wipe out tiger snakes by declaring bounties on kills. But although hundreds of heads and tails have been turned in, numbers do not appear to have reduced significantly. When conditions return to normal again, the snakes retreat to their usual habitats.

The first occasion on record when this was done in Australia was in Tasmania, around 1840, when Lady Franklin, wife of the then Governor, offered to pay a shilling for every snake head handed in. In one season it cost her £600. However, the bounty offer was stopped, not because the wealthy Lady Franklin appeared to be going broke or the snakes were being killed out, but because the authorities said the easy money was demoralizing the island's convicts. In any case, the attempt to wipe out snakes was pretty futile. Tiger snakes, which give birth to their young fully-formed, produce thirty to fifty young snakes in a season, a great many of which must inevitably escape the attentions of birds, lizards and other predators.

There have been many records of tiger snake bites in Australia and the opportunity to study them clinically has been, unfortunately, frequent. Queensland naturalist David Fleay, formerly of Healesville, is one of the many I have heard tell of the effects of a tiger bite. But for Fleay, the bite itself represented an illustration of how carelessness can be dangerous.

Fleay was on his own at the time at Healesville, where he was director of the sanctuary. He was milking a thick, strong specimen about four and a half feet long, as part of the early effort to secure venom for antivenene production. It managed to sink one of its big fangs into his hand. As the amount of venom injected often depends on the size and strength of the snake, this was serious.

Fleay went immediately to the emergency kit. The ligature broke when he tried to apply it. It had been there too long and was perished. He was forced to seek help and this gave the venom time to act.

'I developed a rolling, drunken gait,' Fleay said. 'My vision suffered. It was like trying to look through a wall of water. I was unable to breathe properly. I was either struggling for breath or breathing too rapidly.'

The sanctuary's supply of antivenene was suspect, so more had to be brought from Melbourne, causing a delay of about four hours. By this time Fleay was seriously affected although he showed an improvement immediately he received the antidote. Fleay said the bite continued to affect him for about six months. He felt physically low; he could not sleep without pills; he suffered a nervous breakdown.

Death Adders

With the exception of Victoria and part of South Australia, the sedentary death adders are found over all of mainland Australia and also in Papua-New Guinea. They were probably once present in Victoria as well, but clearing and ploughing of the land has destroyed their habitat.

Three varieties are recognized, all closely related. The common death adder is the most widespread; but there is also a reddish-coloured death adder in desert regions of Central Australia; and a grey to red one in Papua-New Guinea that is generally found in a forest habitat, although it is also notorious in some of the Highlands valleys. The common Australian death adder is grey to reddish, with dark stripes.

The death adder, like the tiger snake, is highly venomous and at one stage claimed a death rate of at least fifty per cent of its victims. Although in favourable areas there are still many death adders around, numbers have declined sharply and they are becoming harder to find. The disappearance of the family from Victoria may soon be repeated in other parts of this country.

The death adder's peculiarity is that he just sits. He lies in the sand or dust, the thick-set body (between two and three feet long for the adult specimen) coiled round in a loop so that his head rests close to the lower part of his body.

The death adder likes sandy or dusty environments where it remains immobile, awaiting passing prey like lizards or small mammals and birds.

On the tip of the tail is a short, articulated spine, looking remarkably like a grub or an insect. The adder can twitch this and make it wriggle in a most lifelike manner, to serve as a hunting bait. Along comes a lizard to snap up what it believes is a grub—and the death adder strikes. Its venom immobilizes and kills the lizard —and another meal has been obtained.

The spine is in no way venomous. It is just a lure, the adder's version of bait. Death adders cannot sting with their tails (an old bush legend) but they can give a good bite from the other end where they keep a powerful venom mechanism. The venom is also strongly neurotoxic, but unlike other Australian venoms, lacks coagulant properties. A typical symptom is paralysis of nerve controls.

The death adder's peculiar danger to man is its immobility and protective colouration. Even experienced bushmen have failed to see it until they have trodden on it. When this happens, the slow old death adder shows a surprisingly quick strike. There is an anti-venene now available to counter death adder venom.

Black Snakes

There are two dangerous snakes in this family, the Papuan black and the mulga, or king brown snake. The third major type, the red-bellied black is less dangerous, although children have died as a result of its bite.

This common black snake inhabits the same coastal area of south-east Australia as the tiger snake and consequently it is found near our biggest towns and cities. It is a rich purplish-black on top, with red or bright orange below. It can attain seven feet in length and this big snake must be regarded as dangerous although generally bites are local in effect. It is also shy by nature and will vanish at the approach of humans if it has a chance. Worrell notes that it will feint rather than strike.

Its two cousins, however, are a more serious proposition. The mulga snake is often taken for a brown snake because of its coppery colour. It is commonly six feet in length and sometimes reaches nine feet. The mulga is found over almost all of Australia, except for the wetter south-eastern coastal zone and is

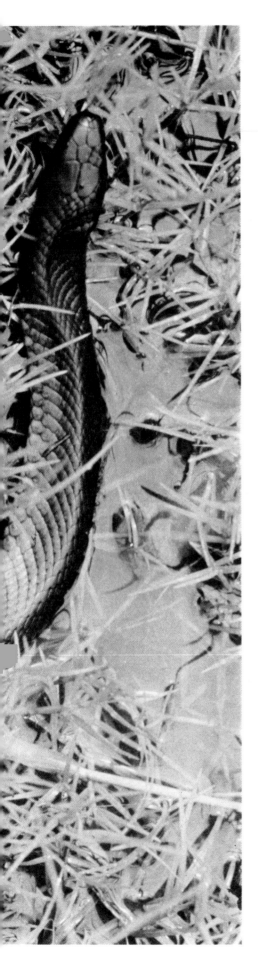

much more dangerous than the common black snake. In tropic areas, it hunts by night and feeds on rats, mice and lizards. It can be mistaken for the taipan, and is aggressive when trapped. Papuan black antivenene will counter the effects of its copious venom.

The Papuan black is the most dangerous of the species and accounts for more deaths in the Australia-New Guinea region than any other snake. It grows to about seven feet and has almost twice as much venom available as the taipan. Fortunately, the venom is not as deadly.

Former ecologist with the Department of Agriculture in Port Moresby, Ken Slater, who has been mentioned previously in connection with the taipan, caught many of these big snakes and said they were very vicious and quick to attack when cornered. Although they are usually a glossy black, they can be a pale or dark brown.

There are two other members of the black snake family, Collet's snake, found in central Queensland and north-western New South Wales, which is of a speckled appearance ranging from pinkish to chocolate, and the blue-bellied snake, found on the western slopes of New South Wales and in southern Queensland. This is black to brown above, with bluish colours below. It grows to five feet, while Collet's snake grows to about six feet.

Brown Snakes

This family is found right across mainland Australia, although the species vary between east and west. The common brown snake is in all the eastern States and south-east South Australia and is classed as very dangerous. The maximum length is generally about seven feet, although a record eight-foot specimen is noted. Colour is generally brown, with regional variations from grey to pinkish shades. It is a slender, fast-moving snake and will strike repeatedly when aroused. The venom is also strongly neurotoxic.

Inland, another species called the western brown snake is found. This is often known by its Western Australian name of gwardar. It is very similar to the common brown. In the southern part of Western Australia, another species

left: A red-bellied black snake in swampy surroundings. This snake is also very common close to major cities but fortunately it is not likely to prove fatal except to children or those with a hyper-allergy.

known as the dugite is common. This is blotchy in appearance.

Early observers of the brown snake family saw similarities with the cobra family, so it was given the name *Pseudonaja* (*naja* is the cobra group).

Whip Snakes

Until recently, the brown snake family was also thought to include the whip snakes. However now the *Demansia* or whip snake genus is thought to be distinctive. One of these, the black whip snake, is found across northern Australia and New Guinea and is probably the fastest-moving Australian snake.

Copperhead Snakes

Copperhead snakes are common in Victoria and are found up through mid-western New South Wales to the ranges around Armidale. They extend westwards into South Australia, where they are sometimes called diamond snakes, and are also found in Tasmania. They are generally a coppery brown, but vary between black and a light copper colour. In New South Wales they are usually between three and four feet in length, but the Victorian and Tasmanian copperheads can be up to five feet.

The venom is highly toxic, but fortunately the copperhead's fangs are relatively small so the venom dose is believed to be limited. Tiger snake antivenene effectively neutralizes copperhead venom.

They feed on frogs, lizards and small mammals but are also cannibals, eating other snakes and even their own young. Copperheads often cluster in tussocks of grass around swamps and, with the shortest hibernation, are the first to emerge in the spring and the last to disappear in the autumn. All authorities agree they are not to be trifled with.

Broad-Headed Snakes

Broad-headed snakes live in coastal areas and mountains of New South Wales and southern Queensland. Their head shape is distinctive among the venomous snakes. They are also conspicuous, the basic black markings being criss-crossed with yellow. Venom is toxic and although little is known about the snakes, as they grow to five feet in length they are potentially

left: The fast striking technique of the deadly brown snake, in this instance goaded by a snake-handler. A brown snake caused a recent fatality in the Murray Valley area of Victoria.

The copperhead, a common but infrequently-seen snake largely found in Victoria. It is noted for its shyness and in many instances, experienced snake-catchers have been able to show that big populations of copperheads were living on farms where the owners believed there were no snakes at all. The copperhead is classed as deadly, but a fatal bite except in the case of a child is unlikely.

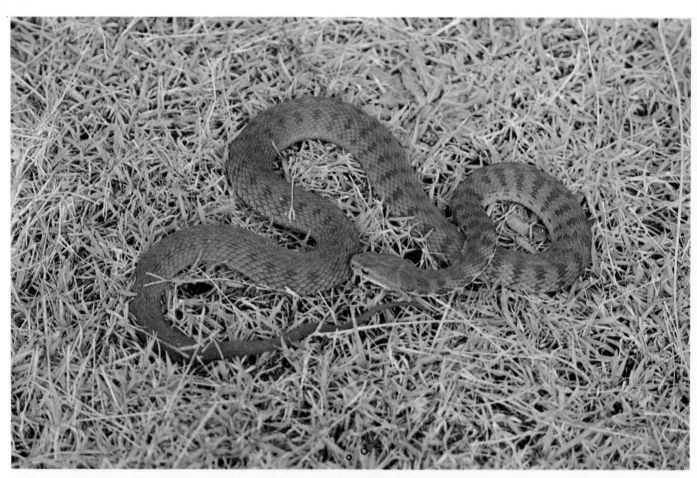

dangerous. They often climb in trees or rocks.

The related Stephen's banded snakes of coastal New South Wales and Queensland, also called locally 'tiger snakes' in some places, are smaller but classed as dangerous to children. They grow to three feet in length. Colouration is brown with broad black bands.

Rough-Scaled Snakes

The rough-scaled, or Clarence River snakes, are usually only about three feet long when mature, but have caused death. They are found in mountainous and plain areas of coastal New South Wales and southern Queensland. Colouration is olive green with dark markings. They closely resemble a harmless type found in the same river bank and swampy environments.

One known fatality from a rough-scaled snake was caused by a practical joker who produced one in the bar of a Sydney hotel and was bitten. The venom attacks the nervous system and is described as extremely toxic. David Fleay was accidentally bitten by a rough-scaled snake at one time, and recalls the pain and swelling that resulted. Tiger snake antivenene can be used in case of bites.

opposite & left: The Clarence River, or rough-scaled snake, which has caused at least one death to an amateur snake handler. Its bite causes extreme pain and discomfort.

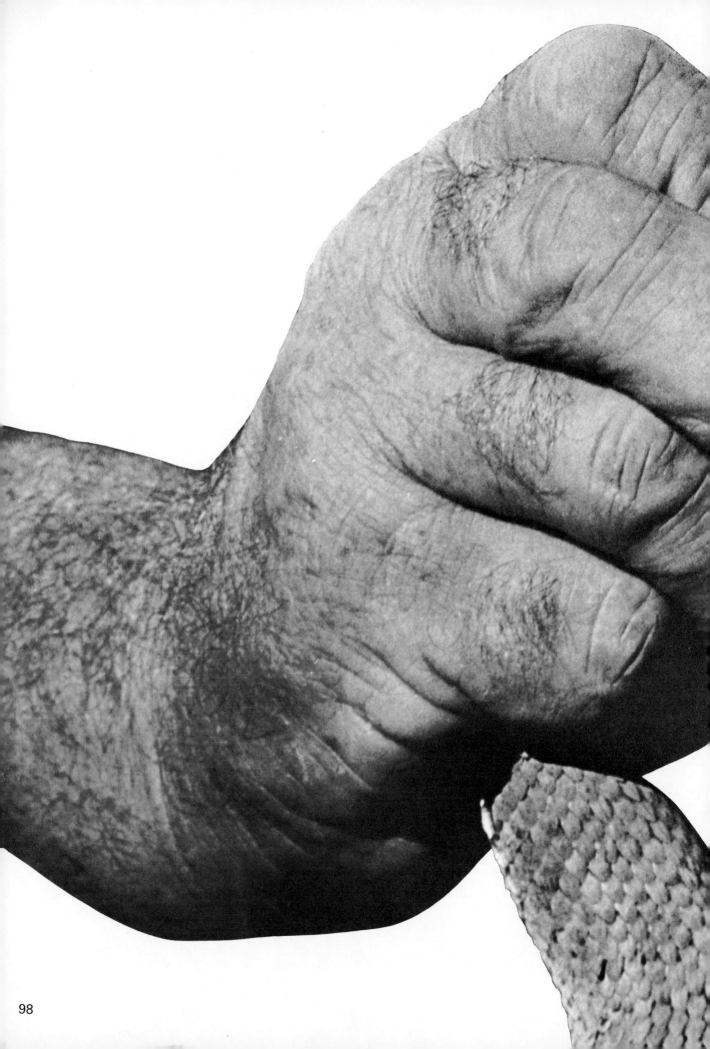

MAN AND
THE SNAKE

Snakes bring out the best and the worst in people. While collecting material on venomous animals in Australia, I met many snake handlers and catchers. It seemed to me that people who are interested in reptiles have many characteristics in common. They were all amateur naturalists—even though some of them like David Fleay and Eric Worrell have built up their collections into big private zoos. But they retain the interest and keenness that is the hallmark of the true amateur. All were also of above-average intelligence and personality; they spoke well and were well read.

Yet there was something else that singled this group out from any average collection of people. One of them put my growing conclusions into words when he said: 'We're all egotists. We like to show off.'

This description—fairly I believe—summarizes the personalities of many of the people I met. There was Garry Zillfleisch in Cairns, Fred Rossignoli, the Victorian temporarily in north Queensland, Worrell, Fleay and the two Cann brothers of La Perouse in Sydney, sons of the late George Cann one of Australia's most famous snake men. Even quietly-spoken Charles Tanner of Cooktown, a contractor for the Commonwealth Serum Laboratories, took on a different personality when I met him in Sydney where at a demonstration to a medical congress he milked brown snakes before an audience of doctors.

There were many others, younger men mainly, who as yet have not developed the maturity and knowledge of these older workers. Some of them, of course, never will. They are pure exhibitionists, relishing the publicity if and when they get bitten, taking risks and showing off and adoring all the attention they get. In the business, they call them 'snakies'. They are a phenomenon that might well be a worthwhile subject for a professional study.

As I see it, the great majority of people have a natural dread of snakes. Without any direct evidence to support this, I would suggest that the human fear of snakes is a genetic factor of our behavioural make-up. Its origin would go right back into our beginnings, probably about the time that the common ancestors of man and the large apes came down from the safety of trees and took up a much richer, but infinitely more hazardous existence, in the reptile-infested grass and savannah woodlands.

The English zoologists, Ramona and Desmond Morris (of The Naked Ape fame) have tentatively explored this thesis and report it in their absorbing book Men and Snakes. For some years they had a television show for children. They decided to stage a competition on which animals children liked and disliked most. Some 80,000 British youngsters wrote in over two years. Snakes easily topped the 'dislike' list, with twenty-seven per cent of the votes. By the way, only 0.6 per cent said snakes were the animals they liked most, 0.9 per cent of the boys and 0.3 per cent of the girls. These latter figures I also regard as most significant.

Keeping in mind the statistic that some 40,000 people a year die of snake-bite in Asia, Africa and South America, it quickly becomes apparent what a positive force for survival an instinctive fear of snakes would be. This would have been even more the case about a million years or so ago when man was beginning his evolutionary development. At that time reptiles were much more dominant than today. If, as some authorities think, this first emergence of man took place in the African savannah, a fear of reptiles when young might have been a key factor in the survival of the species.

But while there is a strong circumstantial case to be made out to support this inherent fear of snakes there is also clear evidence that this fear becomes an attraction in a significant number of individuals. Although these strong behavioural features appear to be opposites, to my mind they are complementary stages of the same emotion. Konrad Lorenz, the Austrian ethologist demonstrates in his classic On Aggression how the bond of love, man's saving instinct, grew out of aggression; how the two drives are basically the same thing. He uses a marvellous phrase, 'man's great Parliament of instincts' which contains within it the idea that our behaviour is governed by the consensus of many forces. It also implies the mutual dependence of opposites through its political analogy.

With this in mind, there is no difficulty in envisaging not only a dread of snakes among the majority but also an attraction to them by a minority. In fact, where you find a powerful instinct of this kind you would expect to find its opposite.

The fear of snakes leads many of us to want to conquer them, for instance. Our first instinct is to retreat but we quickly overcome this and decide to attack the snake and kill it. Conquering a snake is something that sets us apart. While we rationalize it by saying we are protecting other people or removing a hazard, often the killing act is an excuse to give us something to boast about. Garry Zillfleisch has pointed this out quite succinctly.

To a much greater degree, however, this direct attraction to snakes can be seen in one or two individuals in any group watching a snake demonstration. There is always someone who feels a need to catch and handle them. I have seen this phenomenon on many occasions and among many different groups of people—children, doctors at the medical congress, tourists in north Queensland, Government officials in New Guinea and Saturday trippers at the weekend snake shows at Sydney's La Perouse.

Zillfleisch again: 'You can see the looks on people's faces when you handle snakes in front of them. In every crowd, there's one person who will reach forward and pick up a snake. From then on, it's hard to get them to give it back to you.'

Of these only a few ever handle snakes seriously. Some keep private reptile collections (John Cann estimates there are 'hundreds' in Sydney and Melbourne suburbs), others play with them. I would suggest there is a definite way in which snake people develop and although I cannot say with authority that my theory applies to all of them, I feel certain there are recognizable stages which all go through, unless their development is arrested along the way.

Firstly, there is the introduction to reptiles. In many cases, this takes place at a very early age. It probably grows out of normal childish curiosity—and access to reptiles. Many schoolchildren like to catch and keep lizards. They graduate from these to non-venomous snakes, usually when they are in their teens. When they leave school, their interest widens to venomous snakes. This is partly a factor of normal human development, partly one of parental control — and partly economics. To catch and keep venomous snakes you need a high degree of independence and money for snake pits or boxes.

It is at this early stage that 'showing-off' is at its height. The 'snakie' likes nothing more than to have a snake concealed in his shirt and pull it out at a party, or drop it on to a hotel bar for laughs. As the Sydney case of the Clarence River snake showed, this can be a rather hazardous period.

Around this time, maturity fortunately sets in for most 'snakies'. Their interest broadens into an appreciation of nature as a whole. Often they begin a serious study of some aspect of reptiles. They learn the mechanics of scale-counting for identification and collect rare and expensive varieties. Some of course never really grow up; they enjoy the attention their snakes win for them. They become more and more daring—or foolish. Sooner or later, of course, they get bitten—and up to the development of antivenenes, that was often that! Now, however, they live longer and with age and family responsibilities they seem to quieten down, although the 'snakie' often appears to be lurking just below the surface.

The majority that mature become, as I have indicated, intelligent, well-spoken, well-read people — often dedicated conservationists and lovers of nature. One might even go as far as to say that a kind of fellowship develops among most of them. They all know one another; they exchange snakes and letters; they visit one another and there seems to be a grapevine of contact between them.

Many individuals who are interested in snakes keep up the interest as a hobby while they carry out other jobs and professions in the community. They have their own reptile collections and provide the market for semi-professional collectors throughout the country, or they use weekends and holidays to collect for themselves. This extensive collection is having an impact on snake populations in some parts of the country (emphasizing a trend which really begins with the destruction of the natural environment). There are at time of writing moves to protect even venomous snakes in Australia and to licence collectors and individuals who want to keep them. Snakes will then attain the status, in some States, of the more sentimentally protected mammals like the koala and possum.

For some people, the hobby of collecting reptiles can become a mania, just like any other collecting hobby such as stamps or coins. But as snakes are living creatures, the urge to collect 'sets' of different types acquires an unpleasant sort of fanaticism. Occasionally it gives rise to completely unreasonable acts. In 1969 a thief raided Taronga Zoo in Sydney and stole several rare snakes and lizards. These were later recovered from a collector. Snake men with publicized collections are often severely troubled by thieves. They believe only a few are sold. Mostly, they disappear into some fanatic's private hoard. But this fringe element is far removed from snake men with scientific and personal reputations.

The late George Cann is probably the most notable example of the development of a true snake man. He began displaying snakes at the age of twelve.

As a young man, he let his hair grow long and went on the show circuit with his snake collection, in the days when no carnival was complete without its snake act. Often he got bitten—one estimate is about 400 times. But he used quick first aid treatment and survived.

During this time, he built up an immense knowledge about snakes. He then moved over to Sydney's Taronga Zoo, where he became a keeper of reptiles. He still displayed snakes, but the old element of daring and bluster moved out. As he once put it himself, he found that the truth about snakes was just as fascinating as many of the fictions that the professional show men and women spruiked about.

While Cann matured and his knowledge grew, many of his contemporaries died. Eric Worrell in *Song of the Snake* lists many of them. 'That Man' Gray, who had a snake show in Pitt Street, Sydney and his partners Barnett Alberez and George Valves, for example. Alberez died from a tiger snake bite. Valves drew its fangs and died from another bite a month later. He did not know that snakes quickly grow new fangs. And according to Worrell, 'That Man' Gray later died in an asylum for the insane.

Another trio opened at Manly. Cleopatra the Lady Snake Charmer, Tommy

right: George Cann, one of the two brothers who stage public snake-handling displays in Sydney, shows mastery of a black snake.

Wanliss and Anthony Kimbel started as a team which broke up, as Worrell notes, when 'it was not an asp that kissed this modern Cleopatra's breast, but the even deadlier tiger snake'. Wanliss was later to die in Africa from the bite of a mamba, and finally even Kimbel died at Hyde Park in Sydney when a tiger snake fastened on to his arm.

Then in 1913 there was Frank Fox who believed he had found a snakebite antidote. He sailed to India to sell it to the Government but 'a krait proved the antidote useless'.

So the list goes on—all of them early 'snakies' who needed both the snakes and public attention. Most of them bought it at the price of their lives.

For all I know, there might still be snake men like them touring the country show circuit in Australia. I remember seeing dodgers and posters for a show about fifteen years ago. But the modern snake show is a far more sophisticated and a far more worthy entertainment. John Cann and his brother George still keep up their father's show in Sydney on Saturday and Sunday afternoons at La Perouse. A small crowd gathers to see the reptiles they display. But instead of the foolish daring — and the reiteration of faded snake legends—they now attempt to pass on their knowledge and give their audiences something of value.

So too do many other snake displays at recognized public and private zoos around Australia. But the old snake stories and legends are hard to kill and possibly our traditions would be a little poorer if they disappeared.

You will meet many an old bushman, for instance, who will swear black and blue that people he knows have been chased by hoop snakes, which grab hold of their tails with their mouths and bowl themselves along at a furious pace. But in Australia—just as in America where the story is also a favourite yarn—it just is not true.

Then there is the old favourite about the fisherman who ran out of bait and saw a snake catch a frog nearby. He grabbed the snake and poured whisky into its mouth to make it let the frog go. The fisherman grabbed the frog and the snake slithered off. Later, quietly fishing, he heard a polite hissing behind him— and there was the snake with another frog. This one has been told so often that it has the status of a folk legend.

You cannot charm snakes with music. As I mentioned earlier, they are deaf to high-frequency tones. And they do not commit suicide, when cornered, by biting themselves. They are immune to their own venom.

left: At Hartley's Creek animal sanctuary north of Cairns, Garry Zillfleisch demonstrates the milking technique with a taipan. It was in the Cairns area that the first taipan venom was secured by Eric Worrell and his associates.

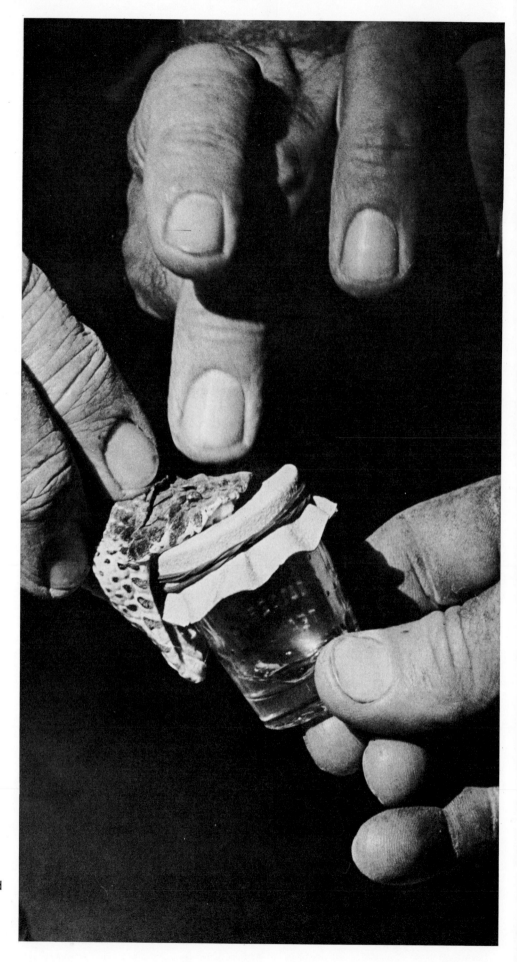

right: Milking a death adder. David Fleay, the naturalist of Burleigh Heads, Queensland, has for many years supplied death adder venom from the snakes in his collection to the Commonwealth Serum Laboratories. The venom is used to make the antivenene, or specific antidote for the death adder's bite.

left: John Cann brings out a group of black snakes at a public showing in Sydney.

right: John Cann plays with a red-bellied black snake. In normal circumstances the snake would make for safety, but as it is here prevented from getting away, it is poised for a desperate strike in self-defence.

Lizard and non-venomous snake bites will not break out in a recurring sore every year. And snakes do not strip cow's udders either. You can find that one in Shakespeare, if my memory serves me correctly. In fact, given a choice of milk or water, thirsty snakes prefer water.

The death adder's tail lure, as I have mentioned, is a bait. It is not a venom fang like a scorpion sting as many bush people will have you believe. And death adders (sometimes with good reason called 'deaf' adders as well) do not leap off the ground to the height of a man's chest when they 'attack'.

Snakes, of course, feature in the legends of almost every culture. In Ireland, where snakes are not found, Saint Patrick, of course, charmed them all away. And in New Zealand, which does not have any either, folk lore looks on Australia as quivering with deadly snakes, which are ready, poised to strike, from the moment the tourist sets foot on the tarmac after he has climbed down the aircraft steps. (In fairness let it be said that New Zealand does not really have as many earthquakes as most Australians firmly believe, either.)

Groups of Australian Aboriginals also have rich legends based on snakes, some of which have been recorded and others which should be quickly before they are lost. The Murray River was dug by a giant snake, one group believes. Others tell of the Rainbow snake in the skies and of evil spirits stalking the earth in the guise of night-roaming snakes.

Then, of course, there is the temptation of Eve—by a serpent of course. The fact that a snake symbolizes the end of the Garden of Eden idyll that brought knowledge and mortality to mankind is another indication, to my mind, of the deep place the fear of snakes occupies in man's make-up. People are not frightened of snakes because of the serpent's temptation of Eve, which they hear about from their earliest years. The story developed as a rationalization of

man's fears. Looked at symbolically, it could even touch a deep core of species memory. The precursors of man descended from a fruit-eating idyll in the forest to a hazardous, tense life as a ground carnivore. This change made man's evolution possible. In the symbol, he was made mortal. And without mortality, evolution would not be possible.

There are similar snake-based legends in other cultures as well. In most, the snake is seen as a cunning, intrinsically evil creature that alters the way of man against man's judgment and conscience.

And, of course, most cultures have given the snake a thrashing as a phallic symbol. This is particularly so in Asia where, of course, snakes are so common and play such a big part in daily life. But even European culture has many stories of serpent lovers that visited girls in the night. In the Middle Ages, throughout France and Germany (according to the Morrises) the devil was reputed to be equipped with a snake-like sexual organ, complete with flicking tongue This enabled him to carry out some rather interesting acts in his continual temptation of woman-kind. Many women accused of having had relations with the devil were burned.

On the other side of the coin, snakes twined round a staff provide the symbol of the medical profession, the rod of Aesculapius. Snakes also played a major part in early medical lore. And in a way, this wheel has gone round a full circle. For once again the venoms of snakes and other creatures are being looked at scientifically. Many believe the biological compounds they contain will benefit mankind.

So from this welter of age-old terror, superstition, and colourful but sadly wrong folk legend, venomous animals are once again being studied objectively. With this change have come dramatic measures that make co-existence much safer for man. And many of these developments are taking place in Australia.

SPIDERS SCORPIONS AND TICKS

Just as snakes instinctively frighten most of us, yet still have their devoted admirers, so too do spiders. If anything, among individuals fear of spiders is even more intense than the general deep-seated disturbance over snakes. We all know people who are reduced to a shivering horror at the sight of a spider —any spider—and even some who cannot bear to remain in the room if spiders are mentioned in conversation.

In Australia, at least, they have some basis for their fears. Known deaths from spider bites are put at twenty-four—ten from the deadly Sydney funnel-web and fourteen from the widely-distributed red-back. Most spider experts add, however, that the figure could well be higher because these deaths have been recorded only when accompanied by a definite identification of the biter. Over the years, there have been many more loosely attributed to a 'spider bite', to an 'insect sting', or possibly even to snakebite.

There is also general agreement that while the funnel-web and red-back are likely to be the only deadly Australian spiders, another ten at least pack enough venom to make you extremely sick, should you get bitten. At least one of these, the *Ixeuticus* house spider is exceedingly common. This spider, now believed to be the same species as the one found in England—and doubtless introduced to Australia in household effects or plants—is strangely enough harmless in Europe. The variety here has developed a venom mechanism which means that these spiders should be treated with the greatest respect.

The Red-Back Spider

The red-back spider was probably also brought to this country as it is distributed right round the world. This spider, *Latrodectus hasseltii,* is probably identical with the American black widow spider and New Zealand's katipo. It also ranges through the Middle East and southern Asia to Indonesia, so it is possible that the spider was established here even before James Cook sighted our eastern seaboard. Wherever this spider is found, it has woven its way into folklore and justly earned a reputation which makes it feared and dreaded.

The red-back probably gave our language the proverb about the female being deadlier than the male. In this species, the female is big and venomous, while the male is only one-third her size —and probably does not survive mating.

The female is a satiny black spider with legs that appear long and slender. On her rounded abdomen is the red stripe that gives her the common name. Among individuals the colour might vary, with pink, orange or even creamy-white stripes being reported. The red-back spins a ragged-looking web, often in rubbish, outhouses, empty tins and under sheets of galvanised iron. What she looks for is shelter from the weather and a flow of air that will carry beetles, flies or other insects into her trap. In the garden, she apparently relishes slaters, those ubiquitous crawly land crustaceans that live under stones and logs. (Another spider species that is potentially dangerous also preys on these common creatures.)

Until you talk to spider experts, it is hard to believe how common the red-back spider is. It can be found almost everywhere. Photographer John Carnemolla, for instance, got one that he used for some of these illustrations in an old garage that a friend was cleaning out, right behind his Sydney darkroom. Keith McKeown estimates that in one small New South Wales town alone, about twenty spider bites a month are treated during the warm months when the danger is at its height. And another spider expert, Ramon Mascord, does not bother to go out to capture red-backs for study. He merely puts an old tin or sheet of iron in the backyard of his home in the industrial suburb of Botany —and the spiders come to him. I would estimate that few older homes in our cities and towns do not have a red-back spider population.

Fortunately, when the risk and the actual numbers of spider bites are known, it appears that the likelihood of getting a serious bite from the red-back is not very great. But the number of known fatalities shows that neither the spider or the bite should be taken too lightly. This, too, is the attitude of the Commonwealth Serum Laboratories, which has prepared an antivenene for the red-back's venom, available through medical centres in most areas.

The red patch of the red-back spider is on the rear of its global abdomen. These spiders are common — photographer John Carnemolla found specimens right in his own backyard.

above: The fearsome-looking funnel-web spider.

The bite is usually marked by a tiny red spot and symptoms start within an hour or so. Like many other venoms, the red-back venom usually causes intense agony. Sometimes there is partial paralysis. A 'pins and needles' feeling in the hands or feet can often last for days. However, antivenene can relieve the symptoms within a very short time and should be secured as quickly as possible.

The Funnel-Web Spider

Australia's other killer spider is the Sydney funnel-web. This is a gruesome-looking spider which lives in the sandstone country in and around Sydney, particularly in the comfortable North Shore suburbs where big homes and gardens take advantage of the attractive rocky hills. However, while this species —*Atrax robustus*—is known to kill, the chances are that others closely related to it are also lethal. These include a big tree-living spider in northern New South Wales which is big enough to relish a meal of frog.

The funnel-web is a big spider. The heavily built female is usually around an inch and a half in length with thick, heavy legs, while the male is about half an inch smaller and is generally of a more slender appearance. Females of up to two inches have been recorded. Notwithstanding size, however, the funnel-web reverses the red-back's deadly female tradition. At least as far as humans are concerned, the male is much deadlier than the female and the ten known deaths are all attributed to males.

One of the reasons for the funnel-web's deadliness is its imposing venom mechanism. The long fangs, which can be shot out into an attack position like a switch-blade knife, are long enough to penetrate clothing and tough skin and can inject venom through their sharp points, just like a snake's fangs. Indeed, the two spider fangs can leave a double puncture wound which can look like the bite of a small snake.

The funnel-web looks for a hole or depression, under sandstone ledges in its natural state, and spins a deep web with a funnel-shaped hole in it, leading

above: A red-back spider and its prey, an unwary insect trapped in the untidy web. The spider can now use its venom to immobilize and kill the insect.

to a lair deep inside. The spiders lurk near the entrance to these holes and capture passing insects or possibly even other ground spiders, stab them with their venomous hunting fangs and retreat to suck out their juices. The dried out husk is discarded, often as litter around the entrance to the lair.

During the mating season, the male is believed to roam in the evening and at night. It can often enter the house. Many are found in cool, dark places like bathrooms. Householders who are used to finding them, recognize the spider's presence by the scratching noise it makes when it scrabbles over hard tile surfaces and have a swift disposal method lined up for it.

One of the characteristics of the funnel-web is its extremely aggressive defence posture. When you corner it, it goes back on its hind legs, with its forelegs, mouth and fangs reared up at the potential aggressor. It will make fast and jerky attacks at a stick or anything you move towards it. Sydney folklore maintains it will jump at you, but I have never seen it leave the ground although

it does lunge at anything that comes within reach.

While male funnel-web venom is deadlier than female, the species still lives up to the spider code when it comes to mating time. The unfortunate male funnel-web approaches mating as one of the most hazardous experiences of his life, one that he is lucky to survive.

When the male comes near the female, she immediately assumes her fearsome attack-defence attitude, rearing up on her hind legs with fangs swivelled out and forelegs menacing. Spider watchers say there is a difference between this and her normal aggressive stance. In mating behaviour, the attitude is more moderate and this nuance of gesture probably signifies to the male that she is ready to accept him.

The male approaches, gently tapping on the female's body. She might retreat from him, but he will stand in front of her, keeping up the tapping. Then, when she resumes her aggressive stance, he will dart in. In the funnel-web and several other types of spider the male has a distinctive set of spurs on his

second set of legs. He uses these to hold back the fangs of the female, which would otherwise pierce and kill him as he approached. Meanwhile, he keeps up the drumming or tapping on her body which seems to send her into a trance.

This continues as fertilization takes place but then, for the male, the really dangerous part begins. With the female's fangs pinned back, he gets ready to leap for safety. The female snaps out of her trance as the spell breaks and often manages to stab the male as he scurries back. In this case, the lover also becomes, as McKeown points out, the wedding breakfast. If the male manages to escape this dangerous instant, he does not linger but flees as quickly as he can. The female then retreats—fed or hungry as the case might be—back into her lair and later produces eggs in a disc-shaped egg sac.

The lethal bite of the funnel-web spider was not recognized until 1927 when a two-year-old boy living in the Sydney suburb of Thornleigh was bitten and died in only an hour and a half. Three more known cases occurred in the next six years—a five-year-old girl and two women. In the other deaths that have occurred since then, children are reported to be common victims.

With both the funnel-web and the red-back, the special danger is to children. The child, of course, is likely to explore old buildings or try to play with tins and treasures found in rubbish tips. Old cubby-houses also make ideal homes for red-backs. And as with all venoms, the effect varies depending on the body weight of the victim. This means that a bite would be much more dangerous for a child than for an adult.

In warning children of the danger, it becomes hard to teach them to differentiate between real and imagined hazards. It is easy to overdo it, even to the stage where they will wake up at night with nightmares. I have tried to steer a middle course by showing my children the dangerous funnel-web and explaining where and why it is likely to be a hazard. We also teach them to stay clear of places that might be dangerous, to wear shoes in sandstone areas around our house and to adopt a few elementary precautions. The simplest of these is to turn over stones and rubbish before you pick them up. I use a stick or garden tool and always turn things towards me. This way, if there is something underneath, it will run away from and not towards me. Heavy gardening gloves are also a good safeguard, particularly in the spring and autumn when funnel-webs seem to be most frequent.

One of the problems of spider bites is the fact that they are likely to occur on the body, rather than on a limb as snake bites do. This makes it harder to apply a ligature. However, if a bite occurs you should always try to prevent the venom flowing through the body by using a tourniquet, if possible. Certainly, suck and wash out the wound.

Seek medical attention immediately. Catch the spider if at all possible (a jar or plastic ice-cream container is ideal) for identification. The general rule is to keep under observation (at hourly intervals at least) any victim of an unknown bite and to get medical attention the

moment any symptoms develop.

There is an effective antidote for the red-back's venom. But the funnel-web's venom, like that of the octopus and the cone shellfish, will not produce antibodies in the laboratories and hence it has so far not been possible to make an antivenene to counter it. For this reason, a known funnel-web bite should be taken very seriously and immediate medical aid obtained.

Other Dangerous Spiders

While the funnel-web and the red-back are the only spiders established as lethal, many others have the potential to give a nasty bite. I have mentioned the house spider. There is a medium-sized spider with a grey abdomen, often carrying a pattern like a brocaded waistcoat, and black legs. It is commonly found in old-fashioned window surrounds, in the bark of trees and around gates and fences. In one case in Sydney, a painter brushed down webs from a factory ceiling and one of this species fell on his hand. He received a bite which incapacitated him for several days. This is a spider which should obviously be left alone.

Dr Barbara York Main, in her pocket-sized *Spiders of Australia* lists several other potentially dangerous spiders. These include the whole of the funnel-web family as well as some of the huntsmen species (*Olios* genus). In many areas of Sydney, you will find spiders of the introduced *Dysdera* genus. These are shiny, cream-bodied spiders with red legs. They prey on slaters, and have a formidable set of fangs which they use for penetrating slater armour and which look as though they could give a nasty bite.

Spiders are members of a special class of animals called Arachnids. Although they get the name from the Greek weaver, Arachne whom the gods changed from a beautiful young woman to a repulsive web-spinning spider because they were jealous of her weaving skill, not all the arachnids spin webs. The class includes two other groups which are dangerous to man. The scorpions form one of these groups.

Scorpions

Australia has a number of scorpions, some of which can deliver a nasty venomous bite, but no cases of resultant death are known. Scorpions got their evil name from the Mediterranean region, where they are found at their deadliest. Australian soldiers in the deserts of the Middle East in the two world wars made their acquaintance at first hand. The danger in these areas is real enough to require the development of an antivenene, which the French Pasteur Institute has created.

Australian scorpions however do not fall into the same order of deadliness. The group is widely distributed through the country. Generally, the biggest are found in tropical regions, and these also deliver the nastiest bite. They should be left alone—an impulse their fearsome appearance encourages.

The scorpion's venom is in its sting in the end of the tail. In an attack, the scorpion will grasp its prey with its big front claws and then arch the tail over to sting. The few who have been stung by big Australian scorpions say that it is extremely painful and that a numb feeling spreads from the wound throughout the body. Some authorities say the venom is similar to that of some snakes.

Ticks

The other dangerous arachnid is the tick. Although tiny, ticks are more dangerous than Australia's scorpions—and their bites are also more than venomous. The different kinds of tick spread many diseases, and they are—from the economic point of view—a far more serious pest than all the rest of Australia's venomous creatures.

As far as humans and their domestic animals are concerned, the worst of these is the scrub tick (*Ixodes holo-cyclus*). This is a tiny, blood-sucking creature which bites into its host and gorges itself with blood. This swells its body, until it drops off to begin the next stage of its eventful life cycle.

The scrub tick needs three hosts during its life. It begins in its 'seed' or larval form, a tiny creature like a dark speck. This climbs on to a mammal—often a cat or a dog—and feeds on its blood. If undisturbed it drops back on to the ground when full and moults. As a nymph, it makes its way to the tips of vegetation in moist areas and climbs on to the second host, again drinking its fill before dropping off. The adult has venom and salivary glands which can inject toxins into humans and animals on which it is feeding. This can cause a severe allergic reaction, paralysis and, in the case of animals, even death.

Scrub ticks are a serious problem in

the eastern coastal regions of Australia, particularly in some parts of Sydney. In the 'tick season', which begins around September, dogs and cats are extremely likely to pick them up. On long-haired animals they are often difficult to find, even though by experience the owner can tell that his pet is harbouring one. Dogs often become listless, develop a temperature and after two or three days can start to become paralysed, often collapsing on their rear quarters. Once seen, the symptoms are unmistakable and frightening.

Scrub ticks can also endanger children. A tick bite is not felt at first, but numbness can spread from the bite and cases of paralysis among children have been known. Among adults, tick saliva can often lead to an allergic condition that can lead to a state of shock and, at best, severe discomfort.

Tick antitoxin is available. In tick areas, parents need to be always on the alert and to search not only their pets but also their children for ticks. If they are discovered and are in an advanced condition, appropriate veterinary or medical aid should be sought.

It is not wise to try to pull off a firmly attached adult tick with tweezers or between the fingers. Often the head will break off and remain in the wound, which means that venom and saliva will continue to flow. This will leave at the least a painful swelling at the site and a continuation of symptoms until the head is discharged.

The recommended practice is to use turpentine, chloroform or some similar volatile to douse the area of the bite with the tick still attached. The tick will withdraw its head and can then be killed. The wound will usually heal simply with

normal treatment and direct venom symptoms will disappear.

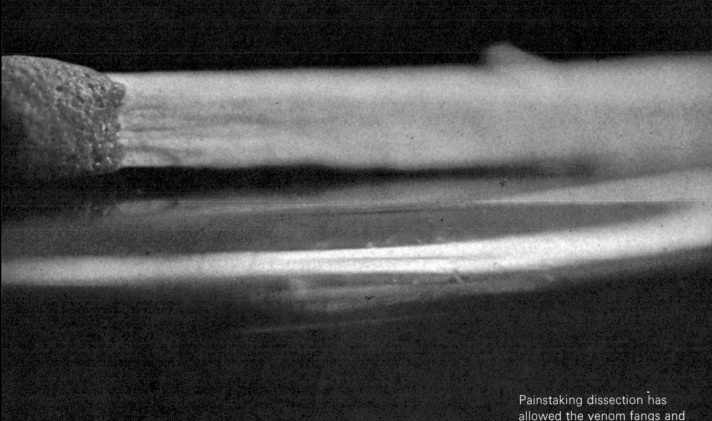

Painstaking dissection has allowed the venom fangs and glands of the funnel-web spider to be removed for study. The size is shown in contrast to the matchhead alongside.

THE

PLATYPUS

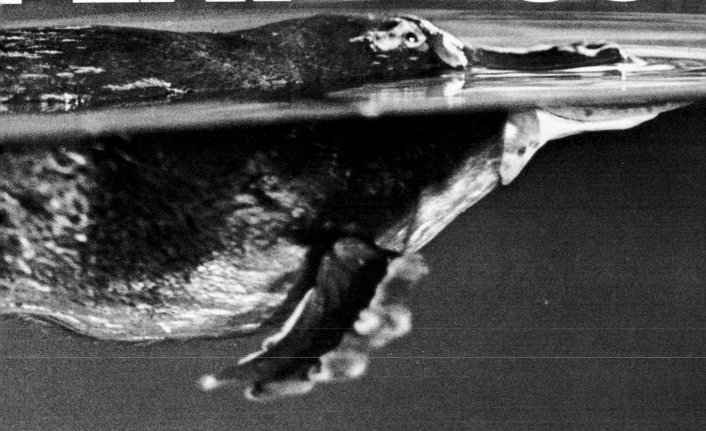

Australia has the doubtful honour of having the most venomous land and sea creatures. It also has a truly venomous mammal.

This is, of course, that living fossil the platypus which has well-developed venomous glands and spurs on the rear legs of the male. The spiny ant-eaters, which like the platypus are also egg-laying mammals, have similar glands, but they appear to be rudimentary and incapable of any effect. The platypus, however, can deliver a nasty and painful sting—although it can hardly be classed as a danger.

There is a controversy among some scientists as to whether the insect-eating shrews, also very primitive mammals, can be classed as venomous too.

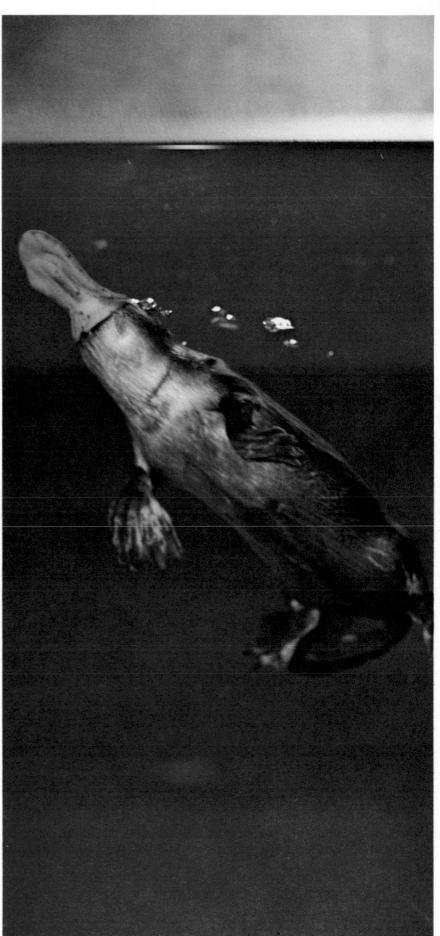

Toxic effects have been noted from the bites of some species. But the general weight of opinion seems to be that this so-called venom is really a potent saliva (which after all is how many venoms developed) and that no fangs or venom mechanism exists. Despite this controversy, however, the platypus can be said fairly to be unique in so many ways that its venom is only a minor feature of its zoological curiosity.

The C.S.I.R.O. zoologist, J. H. Calaby, who has studied the platypus venom, described the venom apparatus as a movable, horny spur, enclosed at the base in a fleshy sheath and normally held against the leg. It can be erected at right angles. The spurs are connected with venom glands. Other workers have noted that the size of the glands varies with the season, being biggest at breeding times.

If you have a close look at the hind leg of an echidna you will see a similar spur. But this is not nearly as well developed and it is doubtful if it could penetrate anything. The opinion of Calaby and other scientists is that it is never used.

The platypus was once found in streams and rivers throughout eastern Australia, but it is now rare and completely protected. You have to go to wild life reserves such as Healesville in Victoria and David Fleay's park at Burleigh, Queensland, to see them. Fleay won fame as the first man to breed the platypus in captivity and has built a special platypus area where the public can see the rare animals. One of the problems is that they are shy and come out mainly at night. For this reason, special conditions must be created so that they can be displayed.

However, their interest to science is much greater than their numbers or prominence would indicate. As far back as 1798, when the first specimens reached London, the platypus has been regarded as a missing link between reptiles and mammals (despite an international controversy at first which occurred among early scientists who thought they were being made victims of a practical joke). In 1884 a zoologist arrived in Australia specially to study the animal and confirm its egg-laying habits. But despite this interest, very little work has been done on the venom.

pages 120-121: A swimming platypus, clearly showing its webbed feet and duck-shaped bill.
right: The venom spur of the platypus.

122

Calaby notes: 'This is perhaps a reflection of the fact that the animal is not dangerous and a fatal envenomation has not been reported.'

Taking into account the rarity of the platypus, its nocturnal habits and its shy nature, the odds are astronomical, one would think, against anybody ever being stung at all. But Calaby claims that about ten cases are known. David Fleay says that several anglers have been victims. They have hooked platypus instead of fish and have been gashed with the venom spurs while trying to set the animal free. Fleay himself has been stung—three times in thirty-four years of studying and handling the platypus. He believes the animal can control its venom release because he has been jabbed on many occasions without any venom effects.

There is little problem in telling when platypus venom has gone in, Fleay reports. 'The result is intense pain,' he told me. 'Agonies shoot up the arm. You wish you had never been born. The pain is ghastly.' Fleay, working among venomous snakes, has first aid equipment ready at all times. He experienced the agony despite being able to put a ligature on immediately and despite taking other steps such as cleaning out the wound. The wounded fishermen, he feels, with no precautions available must have suffered more severely.

Calaby has 'milked' platypus and obtained their venom, which he says is a proteose extract. It can be precipitated into a tiny quantity of pearly white powder. However, he adds, its toxicity is only about a five-thousandth that of a serious snake venom.

It is not yet fully understood why the platypus has venom, why the glands become bigger in the mating season or how the venom is used. The platypus is a difficult animal to observe, but a programme of study is now under way by the C.S.I.R.O. in Canberra. The wild life research division is tagging platypus in little streams to study their travel patterns and has even used small radio transmitters to try to track them—a technique it has used with success for kangaroos and other animals. The unique qualities of the platypus make it a rewarding subject for preservation and study.

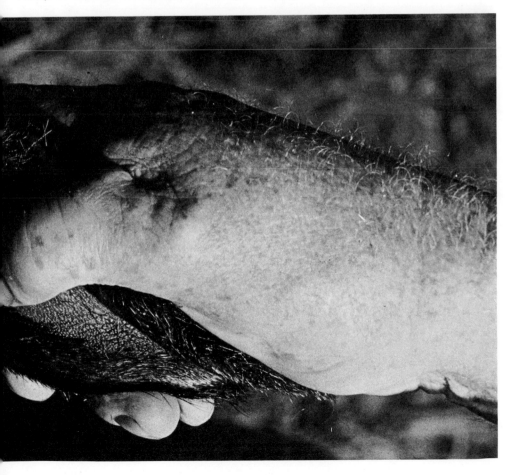

above right: The platypus as sometimes seen by fishermen in quiet rivers, floating like a log or tiny crocodile with its nostrils barely above water.
right: The swimming action of the platypus, near the surface of the display tank at David Fleay's wild life park at Burleigh Heads, Queensland.

above left: After surfacing for air, the platypus. . . .
left: Dives for food, trailing bubbles as it descends.

125

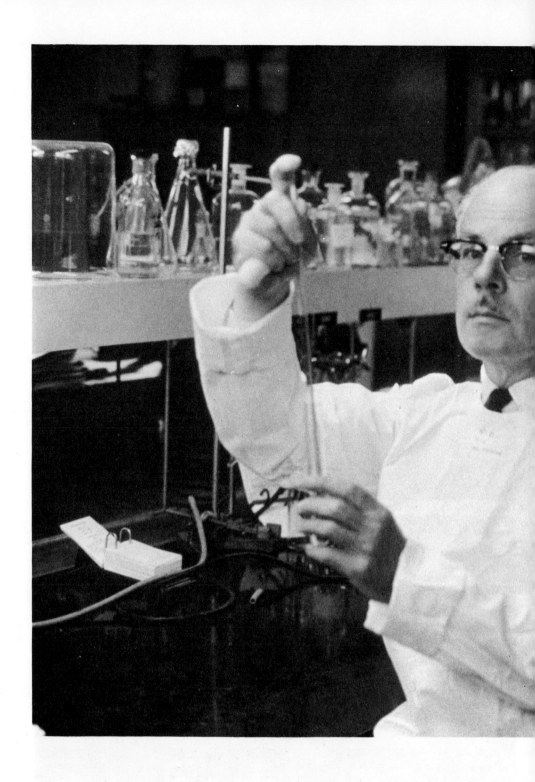

ANTIVENENES

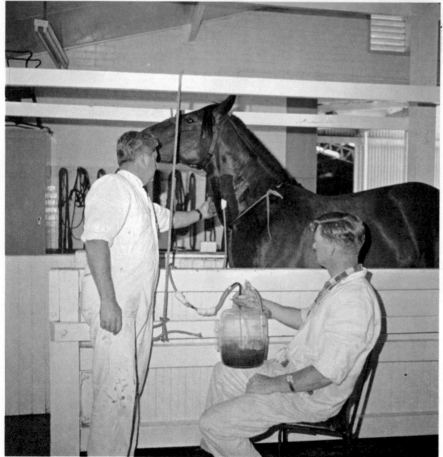

Throughout this book, I have often referred to antivenenes. Now is the time to describe these venom antidotes, how they were conceived and developed and how they are made. Over the years, the Australian Commonwealth Serum Laboratories, in Melbourne, has developed antivenenes which protect against most of the venomous animals in this country. It has been a notable achievement which apart from the direct lifesaving benefits it has brought has also given this country considerable standing in science.

Man's search for effective antidotes to venom goes back at least as far as organized medicine. The American writer, Professor Chauncey D. Leake, of the University of California School of Medicine, has traced snakebite remedies back to the ancient papyri from old Egypt, showing that these were recorded in organized form as far back as 1600 B.C. One papyrus collection at his own university lists 260 prescriptions for treating snake and insect bites.

Many of these were doubtless popular cures. Leek, garlic and onion juice were popular remedies in these ancient times. The Romans also recommended antidotes of this nature. But in the heady rush of nineteenth century science, when the concept of disease-causing organisms was developed and the behaviour of antibodies to counter them was discovered, a scientific basis for venom antidotes was laid. Appropriately the Institut Pasteur in Paris was an early research centre.

Possibly preceding even these French pioneers was the American medical scientist, Henry Sewall who, at the University of Michigan, developed the concept of immunization against rattlesnake venom in 1887. This procedure was the direct ancestor of today's antivenene production. The French were also at work around this time, with the French scientist Calmette a leader in the field. But the French emphasis was on finding a general antidote for snakebite and the discovery that the serums that were developed did not give a broad coverage was discouraging.

Around the turn of the century, Australian science began to make a positive contribution to the field. At this time, settlement was being extended into the northern and inland areas. Human contacts with snakes were common—and often lethal. Snakes were a source of terror in Australia. Writings like Henry Lawson's *The Drover's Wife* were typical: a lonely woman whose husband is away is terrorized by a snake in the house.

Two Australian researchers, Martin and Tidswell, were early workers on venom. They captured specimens of Australian venomous animals, extracted the venoms, measured their toxicity and studied how they worked. From this research, it became clear that venoms from different species differed in their effects. It seemed unlikely that one substance could counter more than one venom. Although this was a discouragement at the time, the emphasis was placed on the track which ultimately led to success—the search for specific antivenenes.

After the end of World War I, Australia had the benefit of two great institutions of medical research. Both were interested in the study of immunology as the body's defence against strange organisms.

One of these was the Walter and Eliza Hall Institute, where research in this field was to lead to the award of a Nobel Prize to Professor F. Macfarlane Burnett. Australian research was ultimately to lay much of the groundwork for the present transplant techniques in surgery.

The Commonwealth Serum Laboratories was the other organization. It had been brought hurriedly into being when the war prevented the import of medical vaccines and was maintained afterwards to provide a centre for vaccine production in Australia and for research into aspects of immunology. Production of antidotes for Australia's lethal snakebites became an early target in this work.

Although the early study had pointed the way in which this could be done—and indeed the technique for producing sera had been known for many years—the producing of antivenenes for some of the most potent venoms known to man was a major project in the 1920s. It was also a dangerous one. Tiger snake antivenene was the first objective and tigers are deadly snakes indeed.

The venom expert Dr C. H. Kellaway

opposite —

top left: At the Commonwealth Serum Laboratories : research into the deadly funnel-web spider.
bottom left: Blood donations from a horse which has been dosed with snake venom. The horse's blood will contain antibodies to combat the venom and these are separated from the serum to become the antivenene antidote.
top right: Measuring out quantities of venom as part of research into venom properties.
bottom right: Microscopic examination of a venom properties experiment.

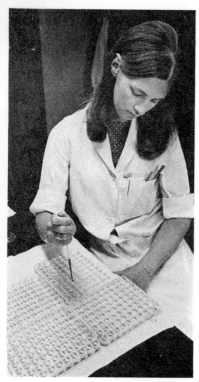

above: Research into sea wasp venom. Samples of blood are measured into containers so that the haemolytic properties can be determined.

was responsible for much of this work. He was able to mobilize the assistance of the group of Australians genuinely interested in snakes—including some of the snake showmen who seized the chance to go 'legitimate'—and the first stage, production of venom began.

When venom-milking techniques had been developed, the storage of venom was understood and supplies became available, the first stage in antivenene production was possible. Using graduated doses, the research workers began injecting the toxin into horses. As the effect of venom on animals is directly proportional to body weight, the horses were able to handle much greater quantities of venom than, say, human volunteers would have been able to. The first doses of venom created immunity in the horses and the doses were steadily built up. With each rise the horses developed more antibodies which circulated in their bloodstreams. Soon, the horses were able to neutralize venom in quantities which would kill literally hundreds of non-immune horses.

At this stage, the horses were bled, just as humans are when they give blood for the Red Cross Blood Bank Service, although, of course, the quantity of blood a horse can give is much greater than that which a man can

spare. These blood donations contained a high proportions of antibodies to counter venom. The C.S.L. men were then able to separate the blood components to acquire a serum that was strong enough, in a normal dose, to give a human victim enough ready-made antibodies to counter the venom he had received in a bite.

The technique sounds extremely simple, but each venom presents its own problems, and the production of tiger snake antivenene in 1929 was a notable triumph.

When injected into the blood of a victim, the antivenene neutralizes the effect of the venom. I picture the way it works as being similar to a dose of an alkali like soda used to neutralize a quantity of acid. A specific antivenene is like this. It exactly matches a specific venom and neutralizes it.

While the secret of obtaining a specific antivenene was the key to making an effective venom remedy, paradoxically it was found that the tiger snake antivenene, while designed for the tiger snake alone, also provided a neutralizing cross-protection on most other Australian snake venoms. In the years after this was first developed, specific antivenenes for other types of snake were also developed, but not

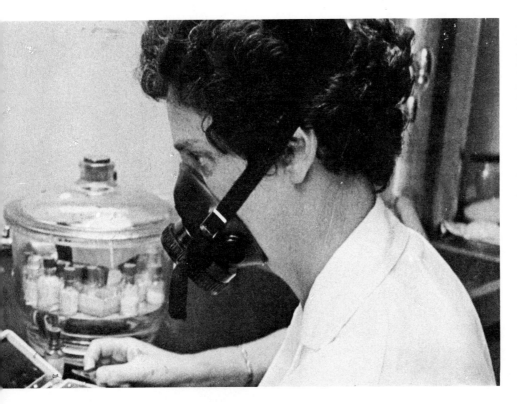
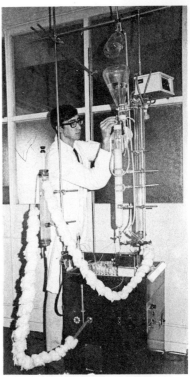

above left: Weighing and dispensing taipan venom. A mask is worn as a precaution against inhalation of the highly toxic substances.
above: One of the stages in determining the constituents of venom at the Commonwealth Serum Laboratories.

issued. Massive doses of tiger snake antivenene were recommended.

The only other new antivenene issued was the tick antitoxin in 1939, which proved invaluable in tick areas. It is still in wide use today, as animal owners in cities like Sydney know only too well.

But despite the cross-protection available from tiger snake antivenene, it was always recognized that it was not the complete answer. One of the problems was that horse serum can cause allergies in many people. And the huge doses needed to counter the bite of a snake which was not a tiger snake were likely to be more dangerous, if only because the amounts needed were so much bigger.

In the 1950s, the realization of the taipan danger led to a revival of anti-venene interest and a specific antivenene for this highly dangerous snake was issued in 1955—with dramatic results from the moment it was first made available.

A brown snake antivenene was issued shortly afterwards. The snake antivenenes were then rounded off with the issue of a specific death adder anti-venene in 1958 and then one for the dangerous Papuan black snake in 1960. In 1961, an antivenene for the tropical sea snake was made available, primarily as a gesture towards the South East Asian countries where these are a major hazard. This completed the coverage of the snake families which are likely to be dangerous in this part of the world. It was found that a large measure of cross-protection between species was poss-ible. For instance, the Papuan black antivenene will neutralize the venom of that snake's close relative, the king brown, or mulga snake. Brown snake antivenene works effectively throughout the brown snake family.

The final step came in 1962. The C.S.L. developed a 'polyvalent' vaccine which would be effective against the major dangerous snakes in Australia. This is now recommended where there is no clear indication of which snake was responsible for a bite. It achieves the ambition of the French and Ameri-can workers nearly a century before by providing a measure of general pro-tection in the case of any snake venom.

But in Australia, of course, snakes are only a part of the venom scene. The C.S.L. researcher, Dr S. Weiner, clim-axed a programme of difficult work in 1955 when he produced an antivenene for the red-back spider. The laboratories produced in 1960 a stonefish anti-venene, largely through the assistance of Queensland workers like Dr Endean.

Horses are kept by the Commonwealth Serum Laboratories at a property near Melbourne to provide stock for antivenene production. The horses are injected with increasing amounts of venom so that they will build up resistance to the venom and this manufactured resistance can be transferred to human snake or spider victims.

In 1969 work was almost complete on an antivenene for the most dangerous animal of all, the *Chironex* jellyfish. This followed a long programme of venom production as a result of researches, mainly by Dr Barnes, described in an early chapter.

Two venoms still defy the C.S.L. These are from the funnel-web spider and the blue-ringed octopus. Both the venoms are of low molecular weight and although C.S.L. workers have tried repeatedly to induce material suitable for an antidote by a roundabout method of substitution, results to time of writing have not been successful.

In the last few years, research into venoms has become more fashionable and several universities in this country are now working on the venom compounds as a whole and on the individual constituents in them. With some venoms, there is evidence to suggest that because of interaction between the constituents, the effect on victims of the venom as a whole is greater than the effect of its different components. In other venoms, however, there is a likelihood that the danger might come from only one or two major constituents.

Interest is also picking up in Australia in investigation into possible medical uses of venoms. Each venom is a unique biological compound with special properties. The Australian snake venoms, for instance, commonly contain substances which coagulate blood, break down tissues and paralyse nerve ends. These could well prove one day to have specific medical uses.

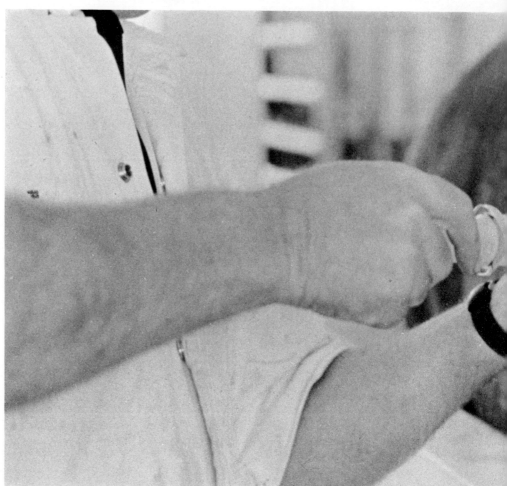

Viperine venoms, which are not represented in Australia, have shown an anti-coagulant property. Medical workers have found that extracts will dissolve blood clots in the human blood stream and this is proving of particular value in cases of thrombosis in pregnant women.

Some of the venom research in Australia is paid for by outside sources, such as the United States Navy. At one stage Australian scientists were critical of one allocation, which funded the study of *Chironex* venom, saying that the fact that it was paid for by military funds obviously meant that the results would be used in chemical warfare. The statement was hasty, ludicrous and sad. A navy which operates in Indo-Pacific tropical waters, where the *Chironex* jellyfish has been shown to be a hazard, has

an obvious need for all the information it can gather on a lethal water creature like this. The United States Navy has assisted much of the work, including the preparation and publication of Dr Bruce W. Halstead's first volumes of the encyclopaedic *Poisonous and Venomous Marine Animals of the World.* Money from Halstead's research programme has assisted other Australian workers like Barnes.

While I would agree that it is a pity our people have to depend on outside sources for funds, the nature of these should not prevent the continuation of the work. I would like to see more money made available from Australian sources. Our record of venom research has so far been good, but with our wealth of material, we should lead the world.

left: Injection of venom into a horse at a dosage many times more than that which would normally be fatal. The horse has become accustomed to the big doses and its system has produced antibodies to combat the venom effects.

FIRST AID

Any Australian who likes to enjoy the bush, the beaches or the tropical coral reefs of our country runs a danger of being bitten or stung by a venomous animal. The odds against a bite or a sting are immense however. You would have to be unlucky—or foolish—to suffer. But the odds are reduced considerably by commonsense behaviour, and in the event of an 'attack', simple precautions can ensure survival.

When you are in the bush—or just around your garden in those Sydney areas where funnel-web spiders are found, wear shoes. To take an extreme case, anyone who goes wandering through death adder country at night without shoes is just asking for trouble. If snakes are rife for any reason (such as flooding which drives them from their normal habitation), leggings and heavy trousers are reasonable precautions as well.

Snakes are shy and retiring creatures, so make plenty of noise. They will pick up the vibrations of your tread, even though they will not hear the higher-frequency sounds of calls and whistles. If you should see one, do not kill it until you are sure it is venomous and then only if you have to. And if you attack the snake, the best thing to do is to make sure you have a good long weapon and plenty of room in which to move. Attacking snakes greatly increases the chance of snakebite. The best thing to do is to leave them plenty of room to slither away—and retreat yourself.

On the coast, the only venomous animal you need to be wary of in southern areas is the octopus. All you have to do is to make sure you do not handle it. If you want to catch an octopus (and from time to time university research workers request public assistance), pick it up with a flat stick or long tongs, like the ones you use in the kitchen. Drop it into a secure container and keep it moist. The best thing to do, however, is to leave it alone.

In tropical waters, the big dangers are stonefish and the *Chironex* jellyfish. You are unlikely to see the stonefish and walking on one is just plain bad luck. However, you will probably escape unhurt if you have good, solid shoes on. Squelching round a reef with wet shoes is messy, but it is infinitely preferable to the dreadful agony of a stonefish sting. If you should catch one in a trawl or net, get rid of it with a long stick or similar instrument.

The *Chironex* is another proposition altogether. It is so dangerous that the onus is on people to avoid making contact. The knowledge that Dr Barnes has gained makes it possible now to predict when the jellyfish is likely to be around tropical beaches. It is best at these times to stay out of the water. But in case a stinging does occur, the first prophylactic is so simple — copious quantities of alcohol—that it is a worthwhile precaution to take at least half a gallon or so of methylated spirits with you whenever you go on to the beach or out in a boat.

No matter how careful you are, the risk of a bite or a sting is always present. Quick and correct action can save life—possibly your own. The following guide is designed to list, firstly, general principles and secondly the first aid action for specific venomous animals.

General Principles for Treating a Venomous Bite or Sting

The objects of treatment are:
(a) To prevent or delay the absorption of venom into the general circulation of the body.
(b) To neutralize absorbed venom with the appropriate antivenene, if available.
(c) To identify the animal responsible to assist in antivenene treatment.
(d) To counter symptoms, particularly the serious dangers of reduction of heart and breathing action which are likely to prove fatal either through the direct action of the venom or through shock. This object is particularly important where no antivenene has been developed (the funnel-web spider and the octopus).

Practical steps:
(a) In all cases — except possibly the stonefish — where the bite is on a limb, apply an immediate tourniquet. A rubber ligature should be carried when hazard is known to exist, but otherwise a belt, tie or padded rope can be used. The tourniquet should be made as tight as possible by some means, for example twisting with a stick. Release for thirty seconds every twenty minutes; discard

after two hours.

(b) Treat the wound. Wash it thoroughly, suck out any venom remaining (if there are no cuts or cracks in the mouth). It is now not recommended that the traditional cutting of the wound to induce bleeding to flush out the venom be carried out. Possibilities of aggravated shock, pain, and damage to tendons and muscles is too great.

(c) Avoid unnecessary movement. Generally, do not expect the victim to walk to help. If he cannot be carried to a car or boat, bring help to him. Immobilize the affected limb in a splint or sling.

(d) Avoid administering liquids. Apply artificial respiration as soon as difficulty in breathing occurs. Place the patient on his side with head down and turned to one side. Make sure an airway is clear. In the case of paralysis, pull out the tongue and depress. Treat for shock symptoms.

(e) Seek expert medical aid as quickly as possible, particularly for antivenenes where available. Antivenenes should be administered only by those with medical skill. There are dangers of allergy and C.S.L. publications indicate ways of overcoming these.

(f) There can be secondary problems with deep bites. Tetanus has been known and also wound infections. These will require special precautions such as anti-tetanus injections and antibiotics which should be administered only by medical authority.

(g) If possible, compile a record of each case, which should be sent to The Director, Commonwealth Serum Laboratories, Parkville, Victoria, 3052. A form is available from the C.S.L.

Specific Treatments

Chironex fleckeri: Popularly known as 'sea wasp', this is a big box jellyfish, found in tropical waters of northern Australia, Papua and New Guinea and Pacific and Indo-Asian islands.

It is dangerous only in the summer months and then only at certain times. The presence of other jellyfish or the small shrimp *Acetes australis* (on which it feeds) are warning signals. Stinging can occur when a swimmer comes into contact with a tentacle, which can wrap around a limb or the body. It is always severe and extremely likely to be fatal.

For first aid, carefully remove the swimmer from the water. Do not attempt to pull off the sticky fragments of tentacle still clinging but sluice the affected area with methylated spirits or some other alcohol. Whisky, brandy or some other spirit will do in an emergency.

Treat for shock; maintain respiration and use external heart massage if necessary. Summon immediate medical aid and start the victim quickly to the nearest hospital. It is often advisable to meet the ambulance on the way.

If the sting is on a limb, apply an immediate tourniquet. It is most essential that the tourniquet be applied tightly. A loose tourniquet will be partially ineffective and will also cause painful swelling. The best places to apply it are around the upper arm or thigh, depending where the injury has occurred.

The tourniquet should be left on if there is a chance of reaching a doctor within half an hour or so, otherwise it should be released for thirty seconds every twenty minutes.

It is most important also that the victim avoids active exertion as, experimentally, panic and flight have been shown to heighten the toxicity of the venom.

At time of writing, no *Chironex* antivenene had been released; however, work was well advanced and there was an expectation that it would be available within a comparatively short time. The antivenene is the only means of neutralizing the toxin. However, even in its absence, medical attention would assist in treating the agonizing pain and other symptoms.

Cone shellfish or octopus bites: In both instances, the bite will hardly be noticeable. Symptoms include numbness, drowsiness, slurred speech and apparent lack of consciousness.

If a bite is suspected on a limb, apply a tourniquet (see above).

Seek medical aid and start out towards the ambulance or hospital, avoiding exertion on the victim's part.

The danger with both these venoms is that the toxin will paralyse the nervous mechanism that controls breathing and the victim will die of suffocation. If breathing becomes difficult, quickly apply artificial respiration, and maintain it. Mouth to mouth resuscitation is recommended. Every attempt should be made to get the victim to a hospital with an iron lung to maintain breathing as—if this can be done—the patient will survive with almost no ill effects as soon as the paralysis wears off.

Capture the specimen if a container is available taking all precautions to avoid a second bite. Beware of carrying either in a pocket or in a cloth bag near the body. Bites through cloth have been recorded.

Stonefish: There will be no doubt when the victim is stung by one or more of the venomous spines. There is immediate and intense pain and a danger of sudden collapse. Immediately move the patient on to comfortable dry sand where he is in no danger of drowning.

Apply a tourniquet (see above) but undo it immediately if it appears to worsen the local effect of the wound.

Wash the wound area and punctures with sea water to sluice off venom and suck the wounds clean if possible.

Summon medical aid and, if possible, start out to meet the ambulance or towards the hospital.

The venom will spread from the wound and there will be alarming muscle swelling and paralysis. Watch for difficulty in breathing and heart stoppage. If necessary, give artificial respiration and external heart massage. Treat otherwise for shock.

If practicable, attempt to relieve the excruciating pain by immersing as much as possible of the affected limb in hot water or by applying hot fomentations.

At medical centres in areas where stonefish are found, an antivenene is available which should be administered as quickly as possible. It will be found that the antivenene will relieve the pain resulting from a severe sting almost immediately.

Snakebite: Doctors now question the value of all the traditional treatments for snakebite and also the snakebite kits of knife and Condy's crystals which were once widely used.

When a bite is known or suspected, immediately apply a tourniquet. As with other stingers, this should be put on above the wound in a single bone area of a limb, for instance the finger, the upper arm or the thigh. It should be as tight as possible and it should be released for thirty seconds every twenty minutes.

Sluice out the wound with water or whatever is available. Suck the wound to remove as much of the venom as possible.

Try—if not risking another bite—to kill the snake in question for identification. At least try to obtain a good description of it including length, colour, shape of body and attacking habit. With specific antivenenes, it is important to have good identification of the biter.

Summon medical aid and start out to meet it if possible. Again, however, avoid unnecessary activity.

Do not attempt to cut the wound again (this can inadvertently lead to damage or the injection of more venom) or to use a caustic like Condy's crystals. Treat for shock. Watch for difficulty in breathing or heart action and if necessary use artificial respiration and external heart massage.

The object of the treatment is to delay the spread of venom as long as possible so antivenene can be administered. This is the only way of neutralizing the venom. It should be injected even if envenomation appears well advanced as there have been instances of immediate improvement at late stages.

Carefully watch all symptoms and record if possible. This is invaluable where it is not possible to definitely identify the snake. The symptoms will often indicate which antivenene should be used.

In the case of a suspected bite, apply tourniquet, clean and suck out venom if thought necessary. If there are no apparent symptoms it is still usually advisable to seek medical advice and aid. It is important to maintain observation on all possible victims for at least twenty-four hours.

Spider bites: Capture the spider responsible in a secure container.

Apply an immediate tourniquet if bite is to a limb. Treat as for snakebite.

Seek medical aid and produce the spider. If this is impossible, give as good an identification as possible paying particular attention to the differences between red-backs and funnel-webs (there is an antivenene for the red-back but none for the funnel-web).

Ticks: Remove tick by dousing with turpentine or kerosene or similar liquid. Do not, as in one recorded instance, try to combine treatment by petrol and the traditional lighted cigarette (which not only removed the tick, but also a considerable amount of skin). If only the body and not the head of the tick has been secured, seek medical aid.

Usually tick bites are not severe, so medical aid generally will not be necessary unless there are causes to worry. However, maintain careful observation at short intervals for at least twenty-four hours.

left: Scrub ticks.

INDEX

Note: Scientific names shown in this index have been obtained mainly from Worrell and from the C.S.L. publication *Venomous Australian Animals Dangerous to Man.* Nomenclature in many instances is still subject to controversy.

Doll's Eyes Snake see Tree Snake, Brown

Dugite *(Pseudonaja nuchalis affinis* sometimes also *Demansia nuchalis affinis)* 78, 93

E

Endean, Dr Robert 44, 47, 131
Enhydrina schistosa 55
Evolution 8

F

First Aid, General principles 138-141; Cone Shellfish bite 139-140; Octopus bite 139-140; Sea Wasp sting 26, 34, 139; Snakebite 57, 140; Spider bite 140-141; Stonefish sting 140; Tick bite 141
Fleay, David **70,** 87, 97, 100, **104,** 123
Flecker, Dr Hugo 24, 25, 32, 33, 35, 46
Fox, Frank 103
Fortescue Fish *(Centropogon australis)* 51
Funnel-web Spider *(Atrax robustus)* **9,** 110, **112-115, 116-117**

G

Goblin Fish (Synancejidae family) 51
Gosford, Australian Reptile Park 60
Great Barrier Reef 44, 54, 56
Gray, 'That Man' 102
Gwardar see Brown Snake, Western

H

Haemolysin 75
Haemorrhagin 75
Halstead, Dr Bruce W. 135
Hapalochlaena maculosa see Blue-ringed Octopus
Holocephalus stephensii see Stephens' headed Snake
Holocephalus stephensii see Stephens' Banded Snake
House Spider, Black *(Ixeuticus robustus)* 110, 115
Huntsman Spider *(Olios sp.)* 115
Hydrophiidae family see Sea Snakes

I

India 12
Institut Pasteur 54, 75, 115, 129
Irukandji sea stinger 32, 33, 35
Ixeuticus robustus see House Spider, Black
Ixodes holocyclus see Tick, Scrub

J

Jacobson's Organs 70

K

Kellaway, Dr C. H. 129-130
Kimbel, Anthony 103
Kleckham, Fred 44

L

Laticauda sp. 55; see also Sea Snakes
Latrodectus hasseltii see Red-back Spider
Latrodectus mactans see Red-back Spider
Leake, Prof. Chauncey D. 129
Legends, Aboriginal 106
Legends, Snake 103-107
Lizards 70, 106

M

McKeown, Keith 110, 114
Main, Dr Barbara York 115
Malaysia 54, 55
Martin and Tidswell 129
Mascord, Ramon 110
Melbourne, Victoria 12, 13, 38, 40, 78
Morris, Ramona and Desmond 100, 107
Mulga Snake *(Pseudechis australis)* 63, 78, 90

N

Nematocysts 28, 29, 34
Neurotoxins 74-75
New Caledonia 54, 55, 56
New Guinea see Papua-New Guinea
New South Wales 38, 78, 91, 93, 97, 112
New Zealand 106
Northern Territory 51, 78
Notechis sp. see Tiger Snakes
Notechis ater ater see Tiger Snake, Krefft's
Notechis ater niger see Tiger Snake, Peninsula
Notechis scutatus occidentalis see Tiger Snake, Western
Notechis scutatus scutatus see Tiger Snake, Mainland
Notesthes robusta see Bullrout

O

Octopus lunulata see Tropical Octopus
Octopus rugosus see Tropical Octopus
Olios sp. see Huntsman Spider
Ornithorhynchus anatinus see Platypus
Oxyuranus scutellatus scutellatus see Taipan

P

Pacific Islands 51
Papua-New Guinea 12, 13, 44, 47, 51, 60, 78, 83, 87, 91, 93